OXFORD *Playscripts*

David Calcutt

the
*L*abyrinth

the dramatized story of
Theseus and the Minotaur

OXFORD
UNIVERSITY PRESS

OXFORD
UNIVERSITY PRESS

Great Clarendon Street, Oxford OX2 6DP

Oxford University Press is a department of the University of Oxford.
It furthers the University's objective of excellence in research, scholarship,
and education by publishing worldwide in

Oxford New York

Auckland Bangkok Buenos Aires Cape Town Chennai
Dar es Salaam Delhi Hong Kong Istanbul Karachi Kolkata
Kuala Lumpur Madrid Melbourne Mexico City Mumbai Nairobi
São Paulo Shanghai Singapore Taipei Tokyo Toronto

and associated company in Berlin

First published 2000

British Library Cataloguing in Publication Data

Data available

ISBN 0 19 831458 2

10 9 8 7 6 5 4 3 2

The Publisher would like to thank the following for permission to
reproduce photographs:

AKG London: p 121; AKG London/Erich Lessinn: pp 104, 111;
Corbis UK Ltd/Kevin Fleming: p 107; Corbis UK Ltd/Gianni Dagli Orti:
pp 126, 127; Corbis UK Ltd/Roger Wood: p 119; Hulton Getty: p 125;
Photostage/Donald Cooper: p 116.

Front cover by Tony Morris

Inside illustrations by Anna C. Leplar

Typeset in Great Britain by Zed, Oxford

Printed in Great Britain by Alden Press Ltd., Oxford

Contents

Characters

In order of their
appearance on stage:

Cretan Chorus 1–6	*a group of Cretans who tell the story and comment on the action in Crete*
Minos	*king of Crete, father of Asterius, Ariadne, Phaedra and Androgeus*
Midwife	*an old woman who works for Minos*
Athenian Chorus 1–6	*a group of Athenians who tell the story and comment on the action in Athens*
Aegeus	*king of Athens, Theseus' father*
The Pythoness	*a priestess, an imposing figure*
Aethra	*Theseus' mother*
Athena	*the goddess of Athens*
Phaedra	*Minos' younger daughter*
Ariadne	*Minos' elder daughter*
Androgeus	*Minos' son*
Nurse	*the woman employed to bring up Minos' children*
Daedalus	*an inventor from Athens*
Talos	*the ghost of Daedalus' nephew*
Theseus	*a young man*
Periphetes * } **Sinis ***	*thugs on the road to Athens*

Sow *   *a wild beast on the road to Athens*

Cercyon *

Sciron *   *thugs on the road to Athens*

Procrustes *

Asterius   *the Minotaur, half-man, half-bull*

Cretan captain   *a ship's captain*

* asterisked characters are marked in the script to be played by members of the Athenian Chorus. They could be played by other actors, to expand the cast.

Pronunciation Guide

This guide aims to show you how to pronounce the names of characters and places in the play, in a way that will be easy to understand. (Some of the names can be pronounced in several different ways: in these cases we have given just one pronunciation, to avoid confusion.)

Where a syllable in a word is stressed, it has been underlined (e.g. as in football, photographer).

TH: this sound is as at the beginning of the word thank-you.

Aegeus	Ij-ee-us	**Minos**	My-nos
Aethra	Eye-thruh	**Minotaur**	My-not-or
Androgeus	An-droj-ee-us	**Mycenae**	My-seen-eye
Apollo	A-poll-oh	**Mycenean**	My-sen-ian
Ariadne	Arry-add-nee	**Pasiphae**	Pas-if-eye
Asterius	Ast-erry-us	**Periphetes**	Perr-if-it-ees
Athena	A-thee-na	**Phaedra**	Fie-druh
Athenian	A-theen-ian	**Pittheus**	Pit-thee-us
Athens	A-thuns	**Poseidon**	Poss-eye-don
Achilles	A-kill-ees	**Procrustes**	Pro-crust-ees
Cercyon	Ker-kee-on	**Pythoness**	Python-ess
Cretan	Kree-tun	**Sciron**	Sky-ron
Crommyonian	Crommy-own-ian	**Sinis**	Sin-iss
Daedalus	Die-der-lus	**Sphaeria**	Sf-eye-ree-a
Dionysus	Die-oh-nigh-sus	**Talos**	Tal-os
Hecate	Heck-ur-tee	**Thebes**	Theebs
Heracles	Herr-a-klees	**Theseus**	Thee-see-us
Knossos	K-noss-us	**Troezen**	Troy-zen
Medea	Mer-dee-a	**Zeus**	Zyoos (*pronounced as one syllable*)
Minoan	Min-oh-un		

Props List

Items are listed in the order of their first appearance, with the name of the character who will use them. See the activity section on staging for activities to do with designing and making masks (page 116).

Act 1

Minos:	crown
Aegeus:	crown
Pythoness:	mask black robe, decorated with feathers and animal bones
Daedalus:	bag/sack, containing: mirror glove puppet winged boy figure

Act 2

Theseus:	sword
Periphetes:	club
Sinis:	dagger
Sow:	pig mask
Procrustes:	axe
Asterius:	bull mask dead cat

Act 3

Ariadne:	knife ball of thread

A Note on Staging

The play is designed to be acted on an empty stage, with perhaps two benches, one at each side, for the Chorus who are not active at the time to sit upon.

You could expand the scenery if required, but as the action takes place in a wide variety of locations, it is important not to let it get too complicated. Large-scale scene changes can interrupt the flow between scenes, which is supposed to reflect the stately progression of the legend.

The script contains simple lighting instructions. However, if you are performing in a situation where lighting is not easy to control, the ends of acts can be shown by the Chorus leaving, so the stage is completely empty.

About the Chorus

The play is structured to use two six-person Choruses, one of Athenians, the other of Cretans. They narrate the story, give reactions and sometimes participate in the action.

The dialogue of the Chorus should flow from one speaker to the next without a pause. Sometimes a sentence is completed by several speakers in turn. Where a line in the script does not end a sentence, this is shown by a dash at the end of the line. The next speaker should continue the sentence, as if only one person were speaking. The best analogy is the passing of a baton in a relay race: the action is continuous as the baton is passed, rather than one person stopping dead and the other starting to move only when the first has stopped.

This 'baton-passing' method of speech can be tricky at first, but it is worth practising to get the effect right. The Chorus actors may find it useful to spend some time in a group, practising only one or two sections, to test out how best to do it. Remember that picking up the speech promptly does not mean that each speaker should read faster than normal; instead, aim to keep a *measured* pace throughout the Chorus speeches. Once mastered, this technique is highly effective and will add enormously to the atmosphere of the play, which the Choruses in particular help to build up.

Map

This map shows the main locations in the play.
In order of their first appearance in the play, they are:

Knossos (Crete)
Troezen
Sphaeria
Athens
Naxos

Act 1
· · · · · · ·

Scene 1

The city of Knossos, on Crete.

*The **Cretan chorus** enter. They speak to the audience.*

Cretan 1	Once there was a king –
Cretan 2	Minos, king of Crete –
Cretan 3	This lovely land set in the wine-dark sea.
Cretan 4	In the city of Knossos lay his palace and throne –
Cretan 5	From there he ruled the wide waters –
Cretan 6	Supreme king, lord of the mountains and plains.

Minos enters. He stands in front of the Cretan chorus, and he too speaks to the audience. His manner is arrogant and emotionally cold.

| **Minos** | Zeus is my father. The blood of gods runs in my veins, and in the veins of my children. I command great armies, a vast fleet of ships. I rule ninety cities. There's no need for high walls around my city. The sea is my fortress. I have nothing to fear. I am Minos the king, and my word is law. |

> *Minos remains standing central as the*
> ***Cretan chorus*** *continue.*

Cretan 1	But on a night of wind and storm –
Cretan 2	When lightning cracked over the mountains –
Cretan 3	When thunder boomed its drum of doom –
Cretan 4	And when waves went crashing over the clifftops –
Cretan 5	On a night of omens and dark portents –
Cretan 6	Fear went rumbling through the heart of the city.

> ***Minos*** *calls out, more annoyed than afraid.*

| **Minos** | What is it? Why this terrible storm? For what reason does this tempest strike my city? Can anyone tell me? Does anyone know? |

Cretan 1	We knew why –
Cretan 2	Us, the people of Crete –
Cretan 3	We knew the reason, and we told him.

> *The **Cretan chorus** now speak to Minos.*

Cretan 4	It's because of the bull that came from the sea –
Cretan 5	A white bull, a year ago, walking out of the waves –
Cretan 6	A gift from Poseidon, the god of the sea.

> ***Minos*** *speaks to the Cretan chorus.*

Minos

I remember it. I remember the day I first saw it. Pure white. Gleaming in the sunlight, so bright it hurt my eyes. Horns shining like gold. Salt water still streaming off its back. I'd never seen anything like it.

Cretan 1

But the only reason the god gave this gift –

Cretan 2

Was for you to make a sacrifice to him.

Cretan 3

He wanted its throat cut, its flesh burned –

Cretan 4

The smoke from that burning flesh rising to heaven.

Cretan 5

Because, although you're a king, he's a god –

Cretan 6

And gods always take first place above kings.

Minos

But I couldn't do it! I couldn't kill such a beautiful creature. Much better to let it roam free among my own herds. I sacrificed another. That was my wish. (*Proudly*) And Poseidon may be the god of the sea, but I am the son of Zeus, chief of all the gods and king of heaven.

Cretan 1

And that's why Poseidon is angry –

Cretan 2

That's why he's sent this storm –

Cretan 3

Because you denied him his gift, and because of your pride –

Cretan 4

And so he's decided to punish you.

> The **Cretan chorus** *speak to the audience again.*

Cretan 5

That's what we told him, the people of Crete –

Cretan 6

But he didn't listen.

Minos

(*With contempt*) So he's angry with me! What's he going to do? Smash the foundations of my city with his storm? Impossible! Sink the whole island of Crete beneath the waves? Ridiculous! Let him rave and spout and rumble and roar. I don't fear him! What can Poseidon do to harm me?

Minos goes. The **Cretan chorus** *speak to the audience.*

Cretan 1   Something far worse –

Cretan 2   That's what Poseidon had planned.

Cretan 3   Far worse than thunder and lightning –

Cretan 4   Than high winds and high waves –

Cretan 5   Something that would strike deep into Minos' heart –

Cretan 6   Deep into the heart of the whole kingdom.

Cretan 1   Because that very night –

Cretan 2   The night of the storm –

Cretan 3   In a room in the palace, a child was being born –

Cretan 4   Minos' child, to his wife, Pasiphae –

Cretan 5   And Poseidon intended to put his mark on that child –

Cretan 6   A mark that no one would ever forget.

The **Midwife** *enters, distressed.*

Midwife   (*To one half of the audience*) Where's the king?

The **Cretan chorus** *speak to the audience.*

Cretan 1   Pasiphae's midwife, she came running from the palace.

Midwife   (*To the other half of the audience*) Has anyone seen him?

Cretan 2   She found us here, spoke to us –

Midwife   (*To the Cretans*) I must find the king –

Cretan 3   With a look on her face, not of joy, but terror –

Midwife	(*To Cretan 3*) Do you know where he is?
Cretan 4	And a note in her voice that made us fearful –
Midwife	(*To Cretan 4, urgently*) If you know, tell me.
Cretan 5	As if some horrible disaster had happened –
Midwife	(*To Cretan 5*) I have news –
Cretan 6	And she was the one who must carry the message.

> The **Midwife** *moves away from the Cretan chorus and speaks to herself, fearfully.*

Midwife But will he want to hear it? The news I have. And when he does hear it – what will my life be worth? Nothing! Best to keep silent. Not say a word. I could go back. Take the creature – wrap it in a shawl – carry it up to the mountainside. It's been done before. And for less. A mercy, it would be. Yes. A mercy for us all –

> *She turns, starts to go, stops, turns back.*

Midwife No – no, I can't – can't go back there, not even for that – seeing it again – and her – I'll run away, then! Yes! Leave here, never come back – but where would I go? What would I do? Been here all my life – there's nowhere else – it's no good – I'll have to stay – pluck up the courage – go and tell him –

> *She starts to move off in another direction. The **Cretan chorus** speak to her.*

Cretan 1 Tell him what?

> *The **Midwife** starts.*

Cretan 2 King Minos you're after, is it?

Midwife The king – yes –

Cretan 3 You have some news for him –

Midwife	News? How did you know?
Cretan 4	You asked us where the king was –
Cretan 5	You said –
Midwife	What? What did I say?
Cretan 6	Nothing – nothing we can understand anyway –
Midwife	(*Relieved*) Good –

> *She makes to go once more, but the* **Cretan chorus** *stop her again.*

Cretan 1	Something about a child, is it?

> *The* **Midwife** *starts again.*

Midwife	A child – ?
Cretan 2	Isn't that what you were talking about?
Cretan 3	And what other news would you have for the king?
Cretan 4	Pasiphae's given birth to a child –
Midwife	Has she, now? And how would you know?
Cretan 5	We heard a cry –
Cretan 6	A child's cry –
Midwife	(*To herself*) A cry – yes – but a child? Can you call it a child – ? There's no name – no name for a creature like that –

> *The* **Cretan chorus** *crowd round the Midwife, worried.*

Cretan 1	What is it, old woman?
Cretan 2	What's the matter?

Cretan 3	What's wrong?
Midwife	Did I say something was wrong?
Cretan 4	The way you're speaking –
Cretan 5	The words you say –
Cretan 6	They fill us with fear –
Midwife	Fear, yes – fear has come – it's here, now, on Crete –
Cretan 1	There's something wrong.
Cretan 2	Tell us – is it Pasiphae?
Cretan 3	Is the queen dead?
Midwife	No – she's not dead – though I think perhaps she wishes she was – poor woman – when she saw it – she pushed it from her, wouldn't have it near her, then took it in her arms again – and cried aloud, weeping –
Cretan 4	It must be the child, then –
Cretan 5	If it's not the queen –
Cretan 6	The child must have been born dead –
Midwife	No – it's not dead – it lives – he lives – but when Minos sees it he'll wish it didn't – wish it had never been born – the best thing they can do is to take it out to the mountain – let the wolves have the beast and put it out of its misery –
Cretan 1	Beast, did you say?

The Midwife realizes she has said too much.

Midwife	What?
Cretan 2	You said beast.

Midwife	Did I?
Cretan 3	What did you mean – 'beast'?
Midwife	Nothing –
Cretan 4	This child a beast?
Cretan 5	What kind of beast?
Cretan 6	What is this beast?

*The **Midwife** cries out in fear.*

Midwife	I can't say – I've said too much – you'll find out – you'll soon know – and then you'll wish you didn't – !

She rushes off-stage.

*The **Cretan chorus** speak to the audience.*

Cretan 1	That was how the news first came to us –
Cretan 2	On that night of storms and portents –
Cretan 3	When the wind shrieked through the streets of the city –
Cretan 4	And thunder roared above the mountain –
Cretan 5	The voice of god announcing his presence –
Cretan 6	The crack of the lightning proclaiming his truth –
Cretan 1	And the truth was this.
Cretan 2	That the child born to Pasiphae that night –
Cretan 3	Minos' son, marked by Poseidon –
Cretan 4	Was nothing more or less than a monster –
Cretan 5	Human body and animal head –
Cretan 6	A child with horns, the head of a bull –

*During the following, the **Cretan chorus** gradually huddle together in one corner of the stage, as if in fear.*

Cretan 1   This was the horror –

Cretan 2   This was the terror –

Cretan 3   This was the nightmare born into Crete –

Cretan 4   The nightmare from which we could not awaken –

Cretan 5   That fell like a shadow upon our lives –

Cretan 6   Across the whole country, a horned shadow.

. . . .

Scene 2

The city of Troezen, on mainland Greece.

*The **Cretan chorus** are seated, huddled, on one side of the stage. They remain there as the **Athenian chorus** enter from the opposite side, and take up a position across the whole stage. They speak to the audience.*

Athenian 1   Once there was a king –

Athenian 2   Aegeus, king of Athens –

Athenian 3   That shining city built on a high rock –

Athenian 4   Above the plain where the olive trees grow –

Athenian 5   City of the grey-eyed goddess, Athena –

Athenian 6   Beset by trouble, a city under siege.

***Aegeus** enters and speaks to the audience. He is a powerful man but worried because his position is insecure.*

Aegeus	I fought hard to secure this throne. But now I'm surrounded by many enemies. My brothers' sons plot against me, wait for their chance to rise and cast me down. If I had a son I'd feel more secure. But no wife that I've married has borne any children. It seems I'm cursed to be childless. Why have the gods forsaken me?
Athenian 1	So one night, as Athens quietly slept –
Athenian 2	In secrecy, under cover of darkness –
Athenian 3	Aegeus, king of Athens, left the city –
Athenian 4	Slipped out of its gates like an outlaw or beggar.
Athenian 5	Robed and hooded he took to the road –
Athenian 6	Seeking an answer among the far, craggy peaks –
Aegeus	Of Mount Parnassus. Delphi, the place of the oracle. There Apollo, god of prophecy, speaks. There, he who sees all that is and all that is to come, will surely speak to me, and tell me how I may get a son.
	*During the following, the **Athenian chorus** close in around Aegeus, creating a half-circle to represent the cave at Delphi. The atmosphere becomes one of awe and mystery.*
Athenian 1	He entered the cave –
Athenian 2	The cave that lay at the foot of the mountain –
Athenian 3	That led deep into the earth's dark –
Athenian 4	Lit by the light of a flickering flame –
Athenian 5	Thick with smoke and the smell of burning leaves –
Athenian 6	Where the Pythoness waited, the voice of Apollo.

*The **Pythoness** enters – an imposing figure, dressed in a black robe hung with feathers and animal bones, her face masked. She speaks to Aegeus.*

Pythoness   Who comes here? Who seeks his future?
                   Here, in this place of doom and foretelling,
                   Who would hear the voice of the god?

Aegeus   I would. I am Aegeus, king of Athens. I seek my future, and
                   the future of my city. I wish to know how I may have a son, an
                   heir to rule when I am gone.

Athenian 1   Then the Pythoness stiffened –

Athenian 2   Her back arched, her eyes closed.

Athenian 3   The flame flared up –

Athenian 4   Smoke filled the cave –

Athenian 5   As her whole body filled with the god's spirit –

Athenian 6   And Apollo's words spoke through her mouth.

Pythoness	Before you return to Athens, Aegeus,
	First travel south to the city of Troezen
	Where your old friend, Pittheus, is king.
	He has a daughter, lovely Aethra –
	She'll be your bride, she'll bear you a son –
	A son to be proud of, who'll rise where you fall,
	Who'll take your crown – a son to be feared.

As the Athenian chorus speak, the
***Pythoness** leaves.*

Athenian 1	Then she was silent.
Athenian 2	The god had spoken, and now he left her –
Athenian 3	The flame died, the cave grew dark.
Athenian 4	Aegeus returned to the light.
Athenian 5	He saw the sun shining above the mountain –
Athenian 6	And his heart leapt, and he rejoiced.
Aegeus	At last! I thank the god for this. I'll go to Troezen straight away. There's no time to be lost. We'll marry in secret, of course. And the child will have to be raised in secret too. If my enemies find out about him, they'll try to kill him. But then, when he's grown, he'll come to Athens, make himself known, and I'll proclaim him my heir. And, as Apollo said, I'll have a son to be proud of indeed!

***Aegeus** goes. The **Athenian chorus**
return to their original places as they speak.*

Athenian 1	A son to be proud of, yes. But also a son to be feared.
Athenian 2	It seems he forgot that bit of the prophecy –
Athenian 3	The ominous part, the sting in the tail –
Athenian 4	For the gods don't give anything for nothing –
Athenian 5	There's always a price, always a catch –

Athenian 6	And the price for Aegeus was to be his death.

Aethra enters and speaks to the audience with bitterness.

Aethra The first time I saw him I hated him. The grand king of Athens, honouring us and all Troezen with his presence. Greeting my father as an old friend – but I could see the contempt in his eyes – for my father, for our small town, and for me. Contempt even as he asked that I should marry him – not asked, demanded! A royal command that must be obeyed. My father owed Aegeus a favour – and I was the price the great king demanded. But I was no bride – simply a womb to carry his son. And later, that night, as I lay beside my 'husband', I would have killed him. Sunk a knife between his sleeping ribs. It would have been no matter. (*She pauses, then speaks more calmly*) But then... then I seemed to dream... a dream so like waking, so like being more than awake, a dream so sharp and clear, that even now it seems the only real thing in the world.

Athenian 1 And this is Aethra's dream –

Athenian 2 The dream she told to us, the people of Athens –

Athenian 3 Many years later, long after it had happened –

Athenian 4 When she was an old woman living in Athens –

Athenian 5 And her future had already taken place –

Athenian 6 And all that remained was this story.

Aethra I woke to dark night. For a long time I lay, listening to the sea. Then I rose, and left the house. I walked out of the town, away from the town, until I came to the shore and the land's edge.

Athenian 1 A little way off there was an island –

Athenian 2 The holy island of Sphaeria –

Athenian 3 Where there was a shrine to the goddess Athena –

Athenian 4	And the island was shining in the moonlight –
Athenian 5	And the whispering of the sea was like a voice calling to her –
Athenian 6	And she stepped from the shore and walked towards the island.
Aethra	I could feel the waves lapping over my feet, rising over my legs, covering my arms and my chest. It was cold and dark and glittering with the starlight, and I closed my eyes to feel its coldness. It was as if the sea had entered my body, as if I was filled with the whole, rolling ocean, the deep sea swell sweeping within me. As if I had become the sea myself.
Athenian 1	Then she waded ashore.
Athenian 2	Salt water streamed from her skin and hair.
Athenian 3	She stood on the island, shivering in the night.
Athenian 4	A small flame flickered in the shrine nearby –
Athenian 5	The flame ever-burning in honour of the goddess –
Athenian 6	And she drew near to the flame, to feel its warmth.
Aethra	And as I did, the flame began to grow. Flickering red and orange and gold, it rose higher, burned brighter, so bright it seemed to be burning the darkness away. And I could see something in the heart of the flame, like a tiny, glowing jewel. And this jewel shone even brighter than the flame. And as I watched, the jewel became a figure, the figure of a woman, and the woman stepped out of the flame and stood before me.

Athena enters as the Athenian chorus speak.

Athenian 1	It was Athena –
Athenian 2	Athena the goddess, daughter of Zeus –
Athenian 3	She stood before her, flame-lit, shimmering –

Athenian 4	And she spoke to Aethra, and this is what she said.

Athena speaks to Aethra.

Athena	You will have a son. Already he grows inside you. And this son will become a great hero, he will be favoured by the gods, perform wondrous deeds. But remember this. Although you are his mother, Aegeus is not his father. The sea is his father, and he is the sea's child. He will carry the power of the ocean within him, and the strength of the waves and the might of the sea. And one day your son will bring death to Aegeus, and on that day you shall have your revenge.

Athena goes as Athenian 5 speaks.

Athenian 5	And, having spoken, the goddess returned to the flame –
Athenian 6	And the flame died, and Aethra stood alone on the island.
Aethra	I left the island and went back across the sea. I returned to my bed, where Aegeus lay. I slept, and when I woke in the morning I remembered my dream of the night before. And wondered then if it had been a dream, and I wonder still. Because it was the most real thing that's ever happened to me. (*She smiles*) And everything that I was told came true.

Aegeus enters to Aethra. When they speak,
Aethra's words are short and clipped,
hiding all emotion.

Aegeus	Aethra. It's time for me to return to Athens –
Athenian 1	So said Aegeus, a little while later.
Aethra	But I shan't be coming with you.
Aegeus	It won't be safe, neither for you nor our child. I have enemies there who'll try to kill you both.
Athenian 2	They stood on the road just outside Troezen, the long road that led to Athens.
Aethra	So, I shall remain here. With our son.

Aegeus	Yes. Bring him up. But in secret. No one must know I'm your husband, or the boy's father.
Aethra	No one shall know. I promise you that.
Athenian 3	And by the side of the road was a rock, a large, red rock, the height of a man.
Athenian 4	And Aegeus drew his sword –
Athenian 5	And lifted the rock –
Athenian 6	And placed his sword beneath it.
Aegeus	When my – when our son's grown, bring him here. Tell him to lift the rock and take the sword beneath it. Then he must come with the sword to Athens. I'll know him, then, and claim him as my own.

Aegeus turns and goes.

As the Athenian chorus speak, they move back to form a small group at the side of the stage.

Athenian 1	And those were the last words they spoke to each other.
Athenian 2	Aegeus took ship, returned to Athens, and she never saw him alive again.
Athenian 3	She never even watched him go. She remained by the rock, and thought of her son –
Athenian 4	The son that was growing inside her –
Athenian 5	Her child, the sea's child, strong as the ocean's swelling –
Athenian 6	And there at the roadside she gave him his name –
Aethra	Theseus. I name him Theseus, king of Athens.

Aethra goes.

. . . .

Scene 3

The palace of King Minos, in Knossos, 16 years later.

*The **Athenian chorus** sit by the stage. The **Cretan chorus** now come forward and speak to the audience.*

Cretan 1   And from Athens to Crete came Daedalus the craftsman –

Cretan 2   The master-builder, maker of miracles –

Cretan 3   To this land of fear and secrets he came –

Cretan 4   With his tools and his plans and his bag of tricks –

Cretan 5   And his mind as crooked as an underground maze –

Cretan 6   To Knossos he came, the court of King Minos.

*Minos enters from one side of the stage, accompanied by his daughters **Phaedra** and Ariadne, and his son, **Androgeus**. Their **Nurse** is also with them. Phaedra is about 8, vain and self-centred. Ariadne is about 12, slightly dreamy but polite and sympathetic. Androgeus, about 10, is arrogant and demanding, like Minos.*

*The **Cretan chorus** take on the role of courtiers at the palace, bowing to Minos and his family as they enter, and listening with interest to what follows.*

*From the other side of the stage, **Daedalus** enters, carrying a bag or sack. He is smooth and confident, not at all in awe of Minos. **Minos**, on the other hand, is rather reserved, and shows some suspicion of Daedalus. **Daedalus** speaks to Minos immediately upon entering.*

Daedalus	I'm here to offer my services to your royal majesty – and to your charming children.
Minos	We're highly honoured. Everyone's heard of you, of course. Your fame comes here ahead of you.
Daedalus	That's very kind. And, by way of making myself even more welcome, I have some gifts here for your son and daughters.

> *Minos' children crowd round Daedalus.*

Phaedra	(*Excited*) Gifts! For us?
Ariadne	(*Curious*) What are they?
Androgeus	(*Demanding*) Let's see them.
Daedalus	(*To Minos*) May I?
Minos	(*Unsmiling, still suspicious*) Of course.

> *During the following, **Daedalus** takes the gifts out of his sack and gives them to Minos' children. He speaks to Phaedra.*

Daedalus	You first. What's your name?
Nurse	This is Phaedra. The king's youngest daughter.
Daedalus	Phaedra. That's a pretty name. This is your gift.

> *__Daedalus__ takes out a mirror and hands it to Phaedra. The **Cretan chorus**, in their role as courtiers, speak among themselves.*

Cretan 1	He's given her a mirror –
Cretan 2	But no ordinary mirror –
Cretan 3	One that does not mist or blur or distort –
Cretan 4	A mirror whose surface is so highly polished –

Cretan 5	As to make an almost perfect reflection –
Cretan 6	To show the face without stain or blemish –
Daedalus	The only face she'd wish to see.

> *Phaedra gazes at herself in the mirror, entranced.*

Phaedra	I'm – beautiful!

> *Daedalus turns to Androgeus.*

Daedalus	Now, young man. What do they call you?
Nurse	This is Androgeus –
Androgeus	(*Interrupting the Nurse*) *Prince* Androgeus!
Daedalus	Androgeus. A good, strong name. This gift is for you, Androgeus.

> *Daedalus takes out a glove puppet and gives it to Androgeus. Androgeus stares at it blankly and Daedalus shows him how to work it as the Cretan chorus speak.*

Cretan 1	He's given him a doll –
Cretan 2	No ordinary doll –
Cretan 3	A doll that moves –
Cretan 4	A doll that leaps and runs and dances –
Cretan 5	Drawing its movement from the movement of his hand –
Cretan 6	Its life from his life –
Daedalus	A doll that lives, or dies, at his command.

> *Androgeus puts the puppet on his hand.*

Androgeus	Look! I can make it move! I can make it do anything I want! I'm like a god!
	Daedalus turns to Ariadne.
Daedalus	And now the other princess –
Nurse	This is –
Ariadne	(*Interrupting the Nurse*) I'm Ariadne.
Daedalus	Ariadne. A proud name. This, Ariadne, is for you.
	Daedalus takes a winged figure out of his bag and gives it to Ariadne as the Cretan chorus speak.
Cretan 1	He's given her a carved figure –
Cretan 2	No ordinary carved figure –
Cretan 3	A winged boy that looks almost real –
Cretan 4	Head lifted, wings raised in the uprush of flight –
Cretan 5	Each barb of each feather sleek and shining –
Cretan 6	As if already piercing the sky's upper limit.
Daedalus	Unfortunately he doesn't fly. I haven't quite perfected that yet. But I am working on it, and one day –
Ariadne	It doesn't matter. I think he's wonderful.
Minos	These are fine gifts, Daedalus. We thank you for them.
Ariadne	(*To Minos*) Are you going to let him stay, father?
Minos	Perhaps –
Ariadne	Please, you must!

| Minos | I'll decide whether he stays or not. Off you go, now, all of you. Go and play with your new toys. (*He speaks to the Nurse*) Nurse. Take charge of them. |

Minos   I'll decide whether he stays or not. Off you go, now, all of you. Go and play with your new toys. (*He speaks to the Nurse*) Nurse. Take charge of them.

Nurse   (*Bowing to Minos*) Yes, your majesty. (*To the children*) Come on, now. You heard your father. But before you go, thank the gentleman for your gifts –

> *Phaedra* and *Androgeus* *ignore her and go. But* *Ariadne* *goes to Daedalus.*

Ariadne   Thank you. Thank you very much.

Daedalus   You're most welcome.

> *Ariadne goes with the* **Nurse**. **Minos** *speaks to Daedalus.*

Minos   It seems that Athens' loss may be our gain. But I wonder why it is you've decided to deprive that city of your services.

Daedalus   The Athenians are savages! They have no appreciation of fine workmanship. A superior craftsman like myself needs to work in an altogether more cultured and refined situation.

Minos   Such as Crete.

Daedalus	(*Putting down his bag*) Such as Crete. Here, I know, my work will be truly appreciated.
Minos	And is this the only reason for your coming here?
Daedalus	What other might there be?
Minos	We have heard... rumours.
Daedalus	(*Innocently*) Rumours?

> The **Cretan chorus**, *still as courtiers, gossip among themselves.*

Cretan 1	Rumours. We've heard them –
Cretan 2	Scandal travels fast –
Cretan 3	How he had to leave Athens in a hurry –
Cretan 4	Fled from there under some kind of shadow –
Cretan 5	Crossed the sea an outlaw, a fugitive –
Cretan 6	Has come to Crete as a criminal, in fact.

> **Daedalus** *looks round at the Cretan chorus, but is not disconcerted. He shrugs.*

Daedalus	It's true. I won't deny it. I was accused there. But being accused doesn't make you guilty. And I am completely innocent of the charges the Athenians brought against me.
Minos	And what were these charges? What is the crime you're innocent of?
Daedalus	I have a feeling you already know.
Minos	Perhaps I do. But I'd like to hear it from your own lips.
Daedalus	Very well. I've nothing to hide. Seeing as the charges were without foundation.

Minos	And these foundationless charges were?

Again the **Cretan chorus** *gossip among themselves.*

Cretan 1	Murder.
Cretan 2	That's what we've heard –
Cretan 3	That's the story that's going round.
Cretan 4	He killed someone, back there in Athens –
Cretan 5	And had to flee in fear of his life –
Cretan 6	And he's nothing more or less than a common murderer.
Daedalus	(*To the chorus, indignant*) Not common! (*Suddenly remembering himself*) And I take exception to the word 'murderer'.
Minos	But you did kill someone?
Daedalus	If you mean by that, did I bring about someone's death, then I won't lie to you. Yes, I did. But it was entirely by accident. And you will admit there's the world of difference between accidental death and murder.
Minos	And who was this person whose death you brought about accidentally?
Daedalus	(*Quite unemotional*) Someone I loved most dearly. That's what makes the charge of murder so ridiculous. Why should I murder someone I loved? Why should I kill a member of my own family?

The **Cretan chorus** *continue gossiping.*

Cretan 1	His nephew, that's who it was –
Cretan 2	A young man called Talos –
Cretan 3	Daedalus' sister's son.

Cretan 4	And Talos, like Daedalus, was also a craftsman –
Daedalus	He was indeed. I taught him myself.
Cretan 5	And, some said, superior to his uncle –
Daedalus	He thought he was superior. There is a difference.
Cretan 6	And that was the reason that Daedalus killed him.
Daedalus	(*Rounding angrily on the chorus*) But it's not true! I didn't kill him. I told you, it was an accident. (*More smoothly, to Minos*) If anything killed Talos it was his own arrogance. That was his problem all along. Nobody could teach him anything. The things he made, they were too intricate, too complex. They never worked properly. They kept breaking down and falling apart. One step at a time, I used to say to him. You have to walk before you can run. But even running was too slow for Talos. He wanted to fly.
Minos	To fly?
Daedalus	He made a pair of wings and said he was going to fly. I told him they wouldn't work. But would he listen? He insisted on trying them out. Early one morning he climbed a rock that stands above the city. I saw him and went up after him. I thought I might be able to stop him, but it was too late. He was standing at the rock's edge with the wings on his arms. I called out, tried to pull him back. But he leapt off the rock before I could get to him. I looked over the edge. I saw him falling, tumbling, trying to flap those useless wings. They just fell to pieces. The rock's high. I think he was dead before he reached the bottom.

*The **Cretan chorus** speak to the audience.*

Cretan 1	That's what Daedalus told the people of Athens –
Cretan 2	When he stood before them, accused of murder –
Cretan 3	And they listened in silence –
Cretan 4	They heard him out –

Cretan 5	And when he'd finished his story –
Cretan 6	This is what the Athenians said:

> *The **Athenian chorus** rise as a body and speak to Daedalus.*

Athenian 1	With all respect, Daedalus, we think you're a liar.
Athenian 2	A liar, and a murderer.
Athenian 3	Your nephew's death was no accident –
Athenian 4	You pushed him from the rock –
Athenian 5	You threw him down –
Athenian 6	We find you guilty of the murder of Talos.

> *The **Athenian chorus** sit. The **Cretan chorus** speak to Daedalus.*

Cretan 1	On what evidence did they find you guilty?
Daedalus	(*Coldly*) An eyewitness report.
Cretan 2	An eyewitness? What? Somebody saw you?
Daedalus	So they said. But it was a trick – a trick, you see –
Cretan 3	Who was the witness?
Daedalus	(*Sarcastically*) They called up the ghost of Talos to speak.

> *Amazement among the Cretan chorus.*

Cretan 4	The ghost of Talos spoke at your trial?
Daedalus	A trick by jealous enemies.
Cretan 5	What did he say?
Daedalus	Only a gullible fool would have fallen for it!

| Cretan 6 | What did he say? |

| Daedalus | You can't expect me to repeat such rubbish. |

| Minos | (*Bellowing*) What did he say? |

In the silence which falls on Minos' words,
***Talos** steps suddenly into centre stage.*

| Talos | I am Talos, the spirit of Talos, his wraith called up from Death's dark halls. Hear the voice of the dead who cannot lie. (*Pointing at Daedalus*) That man murdered me. Daedalus killed me. |

*The **Cretan chorus** react in horror.*

| Talos | My uncle pretended to be thrilled with my invention. He encouraged me, was eager for me to try it out. We climbed the rock together in the morning. He spoke of the wonder it would be, to see a boy flying above the city. I fastened the wings to my arms. He secured the straps, then said all was ready. I leapt from the height. And then realized how he had betrayed me. Instead of tightening the straps, he'd loosened them. The wings fell from my arms, and I dropped to my death. Killed by him. I come now seeking vengeance. I come to accuse. Him! My uncle. Daedalus. The murderer. |

***Talos** turns and leaves. The **Cretan**
chorus stare at Daedalus, horrified.*
***Minos** watches calmly, arms folded.*

| Minos | And now you offer your services to us? |

***Daedalus** says nothing. **Minos** continues
to watch him coldly. At last he speaks.*

| Minos | Do you think it matters to me if you killed your nephew or not? Or if the Athenians found you guilty? A crime in Athens is no crime here. And I have no love for the Athenians. As I said, their loss is our gain. You can stay. |

| Daedalus | Thank you – |

Minos	I'm sure I'll have need to call upon your remarkable skill and craftsmanship. And not just for the making of children's toys.
Daedalus	Anything, your majesty. Any service you require that's within my power. Anything I can make or design or build – you only have to ask.
Minos	I know, Daedalus. And I shall.

> *Minos goes.*
>
> *The **Cretan chorus** step out of their roles as courtiers, and speak to the audience as chorus again.*

Cretan 1	And that was how Daedalus came to Crete –
Cretan 2	Country of fear and shadows and secrets –
Cretan 3	How he found himself here, a stranger in our land –
Cretan 4	With the tools of his trade and his bag of tricks –
Cretan 5	Running from one nightmare into another –
Cretan 6	A nightmare that spoke with the voice of a bull.

> *Off-stage, we hear a low, deep sound, like the distant bellowing of a bull. **Daedalus** stiffens when he hears it, then picks up his bag, and goes.*
>
> *The lights dim to blackout.*

• •

Act 2
·······

Scene 1

> *The city of Athens, on mainland Greece. A year later.*
>
> *The **Athenian chorus** enter and speak to each other.*

Athenian 1	Have you heard the news?
Athenian 2	It's all over the city.
Athenian 3	Everyone's talking about it.
Athenian 4	Everyone's talking about him.
Athenian 5	A hero, fit to rival Heracles.
Athenian 6	A hero, here in our own city of Athens.
Athenian 1	But who is this hero?
Athenian 2	What's his name?
Athenian 3	Where does he come from?
Athenian 4	What great feats has he performed?
Athenian 5	No need to ask, we'll soon find out.
Athenian 6	I can see him. He's coming this way.

> *During the above, **Theseus** has entered. He carries a sword, and speaks to the Athenian chorus.*

Theseus	My name's Theseus, and I come from Troezen.

> *The **Athenian chorus** speak to the audience.*

Athenian 1   And that was the first time that we saw him –

Athenian 2   The man who was destined to become our king –

Athenian 3   Hardly more than a lad, then, standing before us –

Athenian 4   With the dust from his journey still on his feet –

Athenian 5   But a pride in his features, and a light in his eye –

Athenian 6   And fresh scars on his body, and a story to tell.

Theseus   Aethra is my mother, daughter of Pittheus, king of Troezen.
                      Together they raised me. I never knew of a father. On the
                      morning of my sixteenth birthday, my mother took to me to a
                      place just outside the town, where a large rock stood next to
                      the road. 'Lift up that rock,' she said to me, 'and take what you
                      find beneath it.'

Athenian 1   And that's just what he did –

Athenian 2   Without thought or question.

Athenian 3   He lifted the rock –

Athenian 4   A rock neither you nor I could even budge –

Athenian 5	Lifted it, and rolled it aside –
Athenian 6	And picked up the thing he found lying beneath it.
Theseus	(*Holds up his sword*) This sword. Old and a little rusty. It must have been lying there for years. But no ordinary sword, I could see that. Then mother said I should bring the sword to Athens, and I'd find out who my father was. So I said goodbye to her, flung my lion-skin across my shoulders, and set out on the road from Troezen to Athens.
Athenian 1	The road? Why didn't he come by sea?
Athenian 2	Everyone knows the road's dangerous –
Athenian 3	The whole countryside between here and Troezen –
Athenian 4	Teeming with cut-throats and robbers and bandits –
Athenian 5	Brigands and outlaws – and things far worse –
Athenian 6	And what was that he said about a lion-skin?
Theseus	It was a gift from Heracles. He was a friend of my grandfather and he visited us several times. And on one occasion he gave me his lion-skin. I wear it in his memory, a man I greatly admired.
Athenian 1	Now we know why he took the road.
Athenian 2	He wanted to make a name for himself –
Athenian 3	To become a hero like his hero, Heracles –
Athenian 4	By ridding the road of all its roughnecks –
Athenian 5	And there were plenty of them to be got rid of –
Athenian 6	And the first one he came across was –

Athenian 1 takes on the role of Periphetes, taking up and wielding a large club.

Periphetes   Periphetes the Clubman!

                             Periphetes is a thug and speaks like one.
                             This encounter, and the others that follow,
                             are played with slapstick humour.

Periphetes   If anybody crosses my path, I take my club to them. Bash their
                             skulls in! Spill their brains! And I'll serve you, stranger, like
                             I've served all the others!

                             Periphetes swings the club wildly at
                             *Theseus, and **Theseus** dodges out of the*
                             way, as he narrates.

Theseus   And he swung his club at me. And missed. Swung it again.
                             Missed again. I was too quick for him, too nimble on my feet.
                             Each time he swung, each time he missed. Until he began to
                             grow tired. He raised the club to swing again. I sidestepped,
                             grabbed the club, twisted it from his grip – (*He now has the*
                             club) – and broke his head with it!

                             ***Theseus** hits Periphetes with the club.*
                             ***Periphetes** falls, the other members of the*
                             ***Athenian chorus** catch him and he*
                             re-joins them.

Athenian 2   Then he continued with his journey –

Athenian 3   One danger overcome, others awaiting.

Athenian 4   And it wasn't long before he came upon the next –

Athenian 5   At a place where two pine trees grew close to the road –

Athenian 6   A man with a dagger and a wicked grin –

Athenian 1   A thoroughly nasty piece of work.

                             ***Athenian 2** takes on the role of Sinis,*
                             coming up behind Theseus and putting a
                             *dagger against his back. **Sinis** likes to cause*
                             pain. He thinks he's clever. He isn't.

| Sinis | Sinis! That's my name. Hold it right there, stranger. Take your sword out of your belt. Nice and easy does it. No funny business. That's it. Drop it on the ground. Now step aside. |

> *Theseus has dropped his sword and steps away from it, with Sinis behind him.*

| Theseus | What do you intend to do with me? Run me through the ribs? Cut my throat? |

| Sinis | Oh, no! That's far too clean and simple. What I have in mind for you is something far more messy. Far more painful. Over there. Go on. Now, turn round and watch. |

> *Sinis pushes Theseus away. **Theseus** turns. **Athenians 5** and **6** are recruited by Sinis to stand as the two pine trees, and are bent over by Sinis as Theseus narrates.*

| Theseus | Then he took hold of the two pine trees and bent them over until their tops touched the ground. |

| Sinis | They don't call me Sinis the Pinebender for nothing! |

| Theseus | And he secured them there with two pegs. And I noticed that their branches were hung with bones, scraps of skin and hair, dried human flesh. |

Sinis	Strange fruit these trees grow, eh? The fruits of my labours. And soon, my friend, you'll be growing there among them.
Theseus	And there was a loop of rope attached to each treetop. And this villain gave me a particularly nasty grin, and said –
Sinis	Right. Put one of your hands in this loop, here, and the other hand in this loop here. Understand?
Theseus	(*Acting stupid*) No. I'm sorry, I don't.
Sinis	What? It's simple enough. One hand here, the other hand here!
Theseus	It's very complicated.
Sinis	No, it's not! It's easy. A child could do it. (*He grins nastily*) Several have, in fact.
Theseus	(*Still pretending he doesn't get it*) Could you show me?
Sinis	All right. Watch.

> *Sinis 'attaches' a hand to one of the 'pine trees'. This is done simply by the **Athenian** playing the pine tree taking hold of one Sinis' hands.*

Sinis	You put your hand into the loop of rope. Like this!
Theseus	I think I'm beginning to get the idea. And I assume my other hand goes into the other loop. Something like this.

> ***Theseus** attaches Sinis' other hand to the other 'pine tree'.*

Sinis	That's it. You've got it now.
Theseus	Then what?
Sinis	Then comes the really nasty bit. I loose the pegs that are holding the trees down. Up they go! And up you go with them! One half that way. One half that way. And there you hang, ripped in two. Clever, eh? And nasty.

Theseus	Very clever and very nasty. Like this, you mean?
Sinis	Yes, like – !

> *Theseus frees the pine trees. They spring up. **Sinis** gives a loud scream and hangs suspended between them.*

Theseus	And up he went. One half that way, one half that way. Ripped in two. And there he hung, and there he hangs, food for the ravens and crows. As he deserves.

> *Athenians 2, 5 and 6 rejoin the Athenian chorus. **Theseus** picks up his sword and puts it in his belt as he speaks.*

Theseus	As for me, I picked up my sword, put it back in my belt, and continued with my journey.
Athenian 3	By now beginning to make a name for himself.
Athenian 4	No thug or robber on the road was safe.
Athenian 5	Many lay in wait for him – many got their just desserts.
Athenian 6	And not just bandits. There were fearsome creatures –
Athenian 1	Monsters that dwelled among the caves and mountains –
Athenian 2	Such as the fearsome Crommyonian Sow!

> *Athenian 3 takes on the role of the sow, wearing a horrible pig-mask, coming forward with a cry to confront Theseus. The **Sow** speaks in a high-pitched rant.*

Sow	A monster of a pig! A ferocious brute! Huge, gleaming tusks like half moons! Teeth that could chomp through bone and rock! A hide so thick no weapon could pierce it!
Theseus	(*Wincing*) And a voice that squealed like the tearing of metal!

*There is a loud, high-pitched squealing noise, as the **Sow** prepares to charge.*

Sow

Make ready to die! I am a creature from the old times! Hecate the witch is my mistress! The vengeful Furies feed my hot blood! You're beyond the help of any god! The rage of the ancient past falls upon you!

__Theseus__ draws his sword as he narrates.

Theseus

Screaming, she charged! Screaming, she opened her mouth wide! I stood my ground, let her come close – then thrust my sword deep into her throat!

__Theseus__ mimes doing this. The screaming noise stops.

Theseus

And she screamed no more.

*The **Sow** falls back, then takes off the pig-mask and rejoins the Athenian chorus. At the same time, **Athenian 4** steps up behind Theseus, as Cercyon.*

Cercyon

I see you're good with a sword. But how are you with your bare hands? Care to wrestle with me? You have no choice. My name's Cercyon and no man survives my grip. Let my fingers bite your flesh. Let me break your neck.

__Theseus__ turns to face Cercyon.

Theseus

No. I think I'll break yours.

__Cercyon__ and __Theseus__ wrestle as the Athenian chorus narrate.

Athenian 5

And, of course, that's what he did.

Athenian 6

Otherwise he wouldn't have been here, telling us this –

Athenian 1

How the two of them wrestled on the hot, dusty road –

Athenian 2	And though the bandit was strong, Theseus was stronger –
Athenian 3	And he twisted him round and forced him down –
Athenian 6	And broke his neck, and left him dead.

Theseus mimes breaking Cercyon's neck. *Cercyon* gives a cry, is still, then rises to rejoin the Athenian chorus. *Athenian 5* now approaches Theseus, as Sciron.

Sciron	And I fared no better. Sciron. It was *my* custom to wait for strangers as they travelled the clifftop road above the sea. There I'd trip them, send them tumbling down to their deaths in the waves below, where a giant turtle waited, to feed upon their flesh.
Theseus	(*Stepping forward proudly*) But I –
Sciron	(*Interrupting him, resigned and bored*) There's no need. They can guess what happened. I was tripped in my turn. I fed my own pet. My bones lie white on the seabed. I was the last of my kind. With him around, there's just no place for us in this world any more.

Athenian 5 rejoins the Athenian chorus.

Athenian 6	And indeed it seemed at last that the land was safe –
Athenian 1	All villains disposed of, and Athens on the horizon.
Athenian 2	But it was evening, and dark was falling.
Athenian 3	A welcoming light was twinkling from the windows of a house.
Athenian 4	Theseus approached. He was footsore and weary –
Athenian 5	And longing for a bed in which to sleep for the night.

Athenian 6 approaches Theseus in the role of Procrustes.

Procrustes	(*Oily and ingratiating*) Then you've come to the right place, sir, if that's what you want. For that's just what I have! A bed, for weary wayfarers like yourself. Allow me to introduce myself. Procrustes. I keep this humble guest-house, and have only the one bed. But it is a most marvellous comfortable bed, if I do say so myself. As those that have slept in it could testify. There's not a one of them but hasn't slept long and peaceful once they've laid their head and legs upon it.

*The other five **Athenian chorus** members
make the shape of the bed as they speak.*

Athenian 1	And there before him was the bed –
Athenian 2	And it did look comfortable –
Athenian 3	And very inviting –
Athenian 4	And Theseus was very tired –
Athenian 5	And longed to lie down and just fall asleep.
Theseus	(*To Procrustes*) The only trouble is, it does look a little small.
Procrustes	Yes, you're a tall chap, it's no doubt. But not to worry! I am not without resource, and have a small device back here which will secure your comfort, sir. Lie down and take your ease, and I shall return in a few moments. Then you and this bed shall find yourselves in complete agreement.

*Procrustes moves to the back of the stage,
as the rest of the Athenian chorus speak and
Theseus backs away from the 'bed'.*

Athenian 1	But Theseus did not lie down.
Athenian 2	He hid himself behind the door instead –
Athenian 3	And waited as Procrustes went out –
Athenian 4	And returned a few minutes later –
Athenian 5	Carrying in his hands – an axe!

> *Procrustes returns with an axe. He*
> *doesn't glance at the 'bed'.*

Procrustes   Here's my little device to make your stay more comfortable,
sir. A couple of blows of this shall shave your height, and then
you'll fit the bed most regular –

> *Procrustes raises the axe – still failing*
> *to notice that Theseus isn't in the bed.*
> *Theseus steps up behind Procrustes*
> *and snatches the axe.*

Theseus   No, friend, Procrustes! A poor old man like yourself should
take the weight off his feet from time to time. Here. Have a lie
down in your own bed!

> *Theseus pushes Procrustes back onto the*
> *bed. The rest of the Athenian chorus hold*
> *him fast.*

Procrustes   What are you doing? Help! I can't get up!

Theseus   Stuck, are you? Too big for your own bed? I'd better trim you
down to size, then.

> *Theseus mimes chopping off the head and*
> *feet of Procrustes, as the rest of the*
> *Athenian chorus narrate.*

Athenian 1   So he shaved his beard – right down to his neck –

Athenian 2   And trimmed his toenails – right up to the knees –

Athenian 3   And just for good measure, cut his fingernails too –

Athenian 4   Right up to his elbows –

Athenian 5   And Procrustes lay sound asleep – forever.

> *The Athenian chorus re-form themselves*
> *as chorus, as Theseus speaks. The tone now*
> *changes to become more serious.*

Theseus	Then I left that place, and walked on through the night until I came to Athens. I slept outside the city walls. And when the sun rose I entered the city – but it seemed that my fame had entered here before me. Now you know my story. You know the kind of man I am. A man who'll overcome all obstacles, who'll never let anything stand in his way. And you know why it is I have endured these hardships, and travelled here to Athens – to find the man who left this sword beneath the rock – the man who is my father.

> *Theseus draws the sword. As he does so, Aegeus enters to meet Theseus. The Athenian chorus fall back, bowing.*

Aegeus	Look no further. I'm the man who placed that sword beneath the rock. I'm husband to Aethra, your mother – father to you. I'm Aegeus, king of Athens, and you, Theseus, I'm proud to own as my son. Come with me now. I'll explain the reasons for the secrecy of your birth, and then we'll feast and celebrate, and give thanks to Zeus and all the gods for reuniting son with father, father with son – and bringing home to Athens her prince and future king.

> *Aegeus and Theseus go.*
>
> The *Athenian chorus* speak to the audience.

Athenian 1	Soon the news spread throughout the city –
Athenian 2	Everyone knew, and there was great rejoicing –
Athenian 3	And the celebrations lasted for over a week –
Athenian 4	A champion's welcome for our new-found prince –
Athenian 5	The bold adventurer, fearless, ruthless –
Athenian 6	Theseus the hero, born to be king.

> The *Athenian chorus* move back and sit, to make way for the next scene.

. . . .

Scene 2

Outside the palace of Minos, a few years later.

*Phaedra, **Androgeus** and **Ariadne** enter, as the Cretan chorus speak. Phaedra has her mirror with her, Androgeus his puppet, and Ariadne her winged figure. The three sit. **Phaedra** gazes at herself in the mirror, **Androgeus** speaks to the puppet, **Ariadne** makes her winged figure fly.*

Cretan 1   In Knossos the children of Minos are playing –

Cretan 2   His son and daughters, in the palace yards –

Cretan 3   Under the fierce glare of the Cretan sun –

Cretan 4   Where the shadows of the trees give no relief –

Cretan 5   In this city shimmering with heat and fear –

Cretan 6   A heat that hammers the white stone –

Cretan 1   A fear that drums in the dark earth –

Cretan 2   Hammering and drumming beneath the ground –

Cretan 3   Down in the dark –

Cretan 4   Deep under the palace –

Cretan 5   Under the heat-seared, blinding-white courtyard –

Cretan 6   Where the children of Minos are playing.

Hammering begins in the background, like a steady drumming, and continues over the next speeches.

Phaedra   (*To Ariadne, but not looking at her*) Should I wear my hair up, like this?

Androgeus	(*Petulantly, to his puppet*) Achilles! Look at me when I'm talking to you!
Ariadne	(*Dreamily, to the toy figure which she is holding up*) Higher. Fly higher.
Phaedra	(*Still looking in the mirror*) Or down? Like this?
Androgeus	(*To the puppet*) Stand up straight! And don't talk back!
Ariadne	(*To the toy figure*) Above the earth, above the sea.
Phaedra	(*Still looking in the mirror*) Swept back from my forehead?
Androgeus	(*Still to the puppet*) Pay attention! This is your last warning!
Ariadne	(*Still to the toy figure*) Fly to the sun.
Phaedra	(*To herself*) No. It makes my eyes look too big.
Androgeus	(*To the puppet*) Right! I'm just going to have to kill you again!
Ariadne	(*Dreamily*) The sun, the sun.

> *Ariadne* closes her eyes. She is lost in a daydream.

Phaedra	(*To Ariadne*) Do you think my eyes are too big?

> *Androgeus* repeatedly and violently thumps the puppet on the ground.

Androgeus	Take that! And that! And that! And that!
Phaedra	Ariadne –

> *Ariadne*, still with her eyes closed, is holding the winged figure aloft. She pays no attention to Phaedra.

Phaedra	(*More insistently*) Ariadne –
Androgeus	He's dead! I've killed him! Poor little Achilles!

Phaedra	(*Suddenly noticing Androgeus*) What?
Androgeus	But now he's alive again! (*He makes the puppet jump up*) Look!
Phaedra	You're an idiot.

Suddenly the drumming in the background stops. **Ariadne** *opens her eyes.*

Ariadne	It's stopped!
Phaedra	What has?
Ariadne	That noise! Down there under the ground. It's been going on for days!
Phaedra	(*Not really interested*) They're building something.
Ariadne	But what? What are they building?
Phaedra	I don't know.

The **Nurse** *enters, and speaks to them.*

Nurse	Neither do I, but it's sending me round the bend. Thump and bang, bang and thump, all day and all night with hardly a let-up. It's that Daedalus who's at the bottom of it all. One of his schemes. I'll say it now, I never liked the man, and I don't trust him. Tinkering with this, trifling with that. Every five minutes he comes up with some new-fangled contraption or other. The man just won't let anything be. And your father lets him have his way in everything! Won't hear a word said against him! And now he's come up with this new scheme, whatever it is. Top secret. The noise it makes isn't no secret, I'll tell you that. I haven't slept for a week with all that hammering and banging. It's driving me to distraction! And I'm not the only one. It's sent your poor brother mad.
Phaedra	(*Indicating Androgeus*) He's already mad.
Nurse	Not him. Your other brother, Asterius –
Phaedra	(*Angrily*) That creature is not my brother! He's a monster!

Nurse	Monster he may be, but he's still your brother, whether you care to admit it or not –
Phaedra	I do not admit it! I will never admit it! And if you mention him again –
Ariadne	(*Interrupting her, and speaking to the Nurse, concerned*) Is something wrong? What's the matter with him?
Phaedra	(*Sarcastically, to Ariadne*) You mean you hadn't noticed?
Ariadne	(*To the Nurse, ignoring Phaedra*) You said the noise had upset him.
Nurse	Upset him? He's gone berserk. Broken his chains and gone rampaging around the palace.
Phaedra	(*Starting up, alarmed*) What?
Nurse	Yes! That's what I've come to tell you. And your father says you're to go to your rooms and shut yourself in until –
Androgeus	(*Defiantly*) I shan't! I'm not scared of him! I'll fight him!
Phaedra	You? On your own?
Androgeus	(*Holding up the puppet*) No, silly! The two of us! Achilles isn't afraid of anything!
Nurse	(*Ignoring Androgeus*) Now, come on, the three of you, get along to your rooms. I've told you what your father said –
Androgeus	I don't care what he said! Or what you say! I'm not a little boy, I'm a man, and I can do what I like. And I'm not going to my room –
	Asterius, the Minotaur, enters. He wears a bull-mask, and is carrying something in his hands. Androgeus cries out in fear.
Androgeus	Nurse! Help me! It's him! The monster!

Androgeus hides behind the Nurse.
Phaedra too backs off in fear, dropping her
mirror as she does.

Phaedra   Don't let him come near me!

Nurse   I told you to go to your rooms –

Asterius ignores them, and squats. He
begins to eat the thing he is holding. It looks
like some sort of dead animal.

Ariadne   I don't know what's the matter with both of you. He won't
hurt us.

Phaedra   Won't he? He attacked me once before.

Ariadne   That's because you were tormenting him.

Phaedra   And who wouldn't torment a beast like that?

Ariadne   He's not a beast!

Phaedra   Isn't he? Look at him! He's hideous! And what's that he's got?

Androgeus peers from behind the Nurse.

Androgeus   It looks like... a dead cat!

Phaedra   And he's eating it! Urrgh! The nasty, filthy, horrid brute!

Androgeus   He'll eat us next! (*To the puppet*) Come on, Achilles. Let's get
away from here!

*Androgeus runs off. **Phaedra** takes a step*
towards Asterius and picks up her mirror.

Phaedra   (*Staring at Asterius*) He really is quite disgusting –

Asterius looks up at Phaedra quickly and
growls to warn her away. She cries out.

Phaedra   Help! He's going to attack me again! (*She backs off, stops, and speaks spitefully to Asterius*) Father should have strangled you at birth!

> *Phaedra turns and runs off.* **Ariadne** *takes a step towards Asterius.*

Ariadne   Asterius –

Nurse   Don't go near him, Ariadne.

Ariadne   I'm not afraid of him, nurse. He's my brother. I know he won't hurt me.

Nurse   You're the only one he's gentle with, it's true.

Ariadne   That's only because I'm gentle with him. I don't treat him like a monster.

Nurse   Maybe there's something in what you say. But, like it or not, you've got to admit – he's no natural human being.

> **Ariadne** *looks sharply at the Nurse.*

Ariadne   Which of us is?

> *The* **Nurse**, *disconcerted, goes.*
>
> **Ariadne** *approaches Asterius again.*

Ariadne   Asterius –

> **Asterius** *turns to her, as if afraid she will attack him.*

Ariadne   (*Gently*) It's all right. It's me. Ariadne. Can I sit next to you?

> **Asterius** *nods.* **Ariadne** *sits next to him. He continues eating the dead cat.*

Ariadne   Did you kill it?

Asterius   Yes.

Ariadne	Why?
Asterius	It scratched me. It bit and spat. (*He pauses a little*) And I was hungry.
Ariadne	But we feed you.
Asterius	Hungry for raw meat. Hungry for hot blood. I must have meat and blood. I must tear and rip and eat. It's my nature. I can't help it. (*Pause*) I disgust you.
Ariadne	No –
Asterius	I disgust myself. Afterwards, I feel ashamed. I run and hide. I tell myself I won't do it again. But then the hunger comes. (*He turns his face towards Ariadne*) Look at me.

Ariadne looks into his face.

Asterius	The others can't bear to look at me. My face is hideous to them. I am a monster. You don't turn away like they do. But even though you don't look away, I can see I am a monster in your eyes, too.
Ariadne	(*Still looking at him*) Yet I do not look away.
Asterius	No. And you taught me to speak, and you sing me songs and tell me stories. Like the one about the winged boy.

Ariadne holds up the winged figure.

Ariadne	The boy who flies to the sun.
Asterius	I once dreamed I was him. I stood on a clifftop above the sea and there were wings on my arms. I spread them wide and leapt into the air, and the wind took me above the earth. I flew above the birds. I rose higher and higher, towards the sun, and there was golden light all about me. And then –

> *Daedalus* has entered and heard the above.
> He now speaks to Asterius, pretending to be
> sympathetic.

Daedalus	Then the sun burned your wings and you fell into the sea. I know. I've had that dream myself.

Asterius starts and turns in fear.

Ariadne	(*Reassuring Asterius*) It's all right. It's only Daedalus. He won't hurt you.
Daedalus	Of course I won't. Why should I want to?
Asterius	Because you fear me. Because I'm a monster.
Daedalus	Not in your sister's eyes. She sees no monster. She sees a boy who dreamed he could fly. (*He turns to Ariadne*) You still have the winged boy I gave you.
Ariadne	I said I'd always keep him.
Daedalus	In the hope that one day he might fly? I'm still working on it. But your father keeps me very busy.
Ariadne	The work beneath the palace.
Daedalus	Yes. But that's finished now –
Ariadne	What is it you're building?
Daedalus	(*Smiling*) My greatest work yet. A masterpiece. A web, a maze, a pattern of dancing feet set in stone. It is a thing of power... and a thing of beauty. And at its heart lies – (*He stops, mysteriously*)
Ariadne	(*Eagerly, putting down the winged figure*) Yes? What?
Daedalus	Come and see for yourselves. Both of you. Why not? You and your brother will be the first to witness it.

Excited, *Ariadne* rises, leaving the winged
figure on the floor. *Asterius* stays where
he is.

Ariadne	Asterius? What's the matter? Don't you want to see?

Asterius	I'm afraid –
Ariadne	There's nothing to be afraid of. (*She turns to Daedalus*) Is there?
Daedalus	(*A convincing liar*) No. Nothing. You have my word.

                                                 Ariadne holds out her hand to Asterius.

Ariadne	I'll be with you. I won't leave you. I promise.

                                                 Asterius hesitates, then rises slowly and stands with Ariadne.

Daedalus	Good. This way. Follow me. I'll show you the entrance to another world. A world of wonder. A world of mystery.

                                                 They move off. *Asterius* stops and turns back.

Ariadne	Asterius – ?

                                                 He picks up the winged figure that Ariadne has put down.

Asterius	You left this.

                                                 He gives her the figure.

Daedalus	Come on, now. Hurry. This way.

                                                 Daedalus, Ariadne and *Asterius* go.

                                                 The **Cretan chorus** speak to the audience and each other.

Cretan 1	Listen. The streets of Knossos are silent.
Cretan 2	The air is still, taut as a drawn bowstring –
Cretan 3	And the heat is intense, a blinding haze –
Cretan 4	And the light is merciless, scouring the eyes, numbing the brain –

Cretan 5	Nothing moves, nothing can move, everything lies stunned –
Cretan 6	Unable to stir under the weight of the heat and the light.
Cretan 1	It's like waiting for a storm to break –
Cretan 2	And the silence is oppressive like the approach of the thunder –
Cretan 3	Like waiting for an earthquake to shock through the city –
Cretan 4	And the heat and the light grind together like bedrock –
Cretan 5	And the tension is unbearable –
Cretan 6	And everything is straining towards its breaking-point –
Cretan 1	So we wait –
Cretan 2	We, the people of Crete, wait –
Cretan 3	In the city of Knossos where the air is screaming –
Cretan 4	Like victims prepared for sacrifice, we wait –
Cretan 5	For the snap of the bowstring, the shockwave, the screech –
Cretan 6	For the terrible thing that is waiting to happen.

Ariadne runs on-stage, distraught.

| Ariadne | How could they do it? How could they do such a thing? He knew all along! Daedalus! Planned it, while he was here, talking. I didn't realize! I didn't know. But I'm the one who led him there! I betrayed him! |

The **Cretan chorus** gather round Ariadne, concerned.

| Cretan 1 | What is it? What's happened? |

| Cretan 2 | Something terrible, just as we feared. |

| Cretan 3 | Tell us. Who did you betray? |

Ariadne gathers herself with effort and tries to speak calmly.

| Ariadne | We followed Daedalus into the palace, to the enclosed courtyard where the dancing-floor is. Daedalus made it for me. You've seen it, you know it. |

| Cretan 4 | Yes, we know it. A beautiful piece of work – |

| Cretan 5 | The floor tiled with an intricate pattern – |

| Cretan 6 | A path that winds and twists and curves – |

| Cretan 1 | Weaving in and out to the centre and back. |

| Cretan 2 | We've seen you dance there at the great festivals – |

| Cretan 3 | Your feet following the path's pattern. |

| Ariadne | Yes. I've danced there. But I'll never dance there again. It's a place of horror now. And he led us to it – Daedalus, talking, smiling. He showed us a doorway he'd cut into the dancing-floor, so cunningly made you couldn't see it until it was opened. He opened it, raised it, pointed out the steps he'd made. Steps going down, into the dark. Then, for the first time, I felt afraid. And Asterius. I could feel him trembling. But what was there to be afraid of, I thought? So I turned to re-assure him, tell him everything was all right. And as I did, soldiers appeared. Five or six of them. My father's bodyguard... |

Her voice falters a little and she stops speaking, to compose herself again. Having done so, she carries on speaking. The action she now describes may be enacted on-stage as a dumbshow, highly stylized, or perhaps as a shadow show behind a back-lit screen.

Ariadne   Everything happened quickly then – too quickly – suddenly
the soldiers had taken hold of my brother – they were dragging
him from me – he roared and struggled, tried to break free,
but they were too many, too strong – then they were forcing
him through the doorway – pushing him down, down into the
dark – he looked up at me – it was the last I saw of him – his
face staring into mine – filled with terror, rage – and in his
eyes a look – it pierced me through – a look I'll never forget –
an accusation – then the door slammed shut and he was
gone –

She stops again, composes herself, continues.

Ariadne   That's what they were building. A prison. For him. For the
monster. He's locked in there, now, trapped underground.
He'll live and he'll die there. And in the dark he truly will
become a monster. And I'm trapped too. The palace is a
prison. The city. The whole island, the land of Crete, has
become a prison. (*She shudders*) And all who live here
are monsters.

Ariadne goes.

*The **Cretan chorus** speak to the audience.*
As they do, off-stage, there is a deep,
ominous rumbling sound, that gradually
grows louder.

Cretan 4   And beneath the silence that follows her words –

Cretan 5   We hear for the first time a sound like thunder –

Cretan 6   Seeming far-off, but growing closer –

Cretan 1   A sound like thunder, but not thunder –

Cretan 2   A sound perhaps more like the slow grinding of rock –

Cretan 3   Or the drumming of hooves deep beneath the ground –

Cretan 4   A sound rising up from deep beneath the ground –

Cretan 5   A howl, a sheer animal roar of rage –

Cretan 6   That shakes the earth, that shocks up through our bodies –

Cretan 1   And runs underneath the city, worse than any earthquake –

Cretan 2   And all hear it, and are stunned with fear –

Cretan 3   A voice that cries out from their very worst nightmare –

Cretan 4   The voice of the monster under the ground –

Cretan 5   Hungry for meat, hungry for blood and revenge –

Cretan 6   The voice of the caged beast, the voice of Crete.

The rumbling sound grows even louder now,
a terrifying, deafening roar. Lights go to
blackout, but the roar continues in the
darkness, then stops abruptly.

. . . .

Act 3
· · · · · · ·

Scene 1

The city of Troezen.

Aethra enters and speaks to the audience.

Aethra   My son's gone to Athens, a mighty champion, and made the name of hero for himself. Aegeus, my husband, has proclaimed him as his son and heir. The Athenians have taken him to their hearts. As for Aegeus' enemies – his brothers' sons – Theseus led an army against them, defeated and destroyed them all. So now Athens is safe, and my son even more the champion and hero. All that Aegeus wanted, he's been given. His gods smile on him – and on his son.

Her tone changes, and she speaks with some bitterness.

Aethra   As for me – the mother of this hero, the wife of this king – do I share in the glory? Am I honoured in Athens? Is my name cried aloud in the city streets? My name's not even known! I remain here in Troezen, cast-off, abandoned, forgotten. But I do not forget. I do not forget the goddess Athena's words to me. 'One day your son will bring death to Aegeus, and on that day you shall have your revenge.' So here in Troezen I bide my time, watch from afar – and wait for what will come.

Aethra goes.

· ·

Scene 2

The city of Athens.

*The **Athenian chorus** enter on one side of the stage as they speak.*

Athenian 1   Black ships are coming from Crete –

Athenian 2	Black ships with black sails, coming from Crete to Athens –
Athenian 3	And on each sail, a red bull –
Athenian 4	And a bull's head carved into each prow –
Athenian 5	And the prows are black, plunging through the black wavetops –
Athenian 6	Black ships with black prows, coming to Athens from Crete.
Athenian 1	What do they want with us?
Athenian 2	Why are these fiercesome ships coming here?
Athenian 3	Their coming fills us with terror –
Athenian 4	Black dreams sweating in black nights –
Athenian 5	Lost in the winding paths of nightmare, unable to escape –
Athenian 6	Unable to wake from the beast beating at the skull's door.
Athenian 1	(*Points across the stage*) Look! I see them! The black sails!

Athenian 2	They're coming like birds of death, skimming the waves –
Athenian 3	And the ships themselves, black-hulled, streaming black water –
Athenian 4	Plunging towards us, like vessels out of the dead land.
Athenian 5	What cargo do they carry? What transport of terror?
Athenian 6	What horror is stored in their dark holds?

> *The **Cretan chorus** enter on the other side of the stage as they speak.*

Cretan 1	We carry no cargo –
Cretan 2	Our holds are empty.
Cretan 3	Nothing has been carried to Athens from Crete.
Cretan 4	We come with our black ships empty –
Cretan 5	Only a darkness in the holds –
Cretan 6	Only an emptiness waiting to be filled.
Cretan 1	You fear us. You are right to fear.
Cretan 2	Our shadows fall upon the bright streets of Athens –
Cretan 3	The shadows of our ships darken the waters in the harbour –
Cretan 4	They stand with empty holds.
Cretan 5	We have come seeking cargo –
Cretan 6	Portable cargo – human – fresh meat.

> ***Aegeus** and **Theseus** enter. The **Athenian chorus** bow. The **Cretan chorus** stand defiant, unmoving.*

Aegeus	(*To the Cretans*) What's going on? What are those Cretan ships in the harbour? And what are you doing here in our city? Answer me. I'm Aegeus, king of Athens, and this is my son, Theseus.
Theseus	(*To the Cretans*) You have a dangerous look about you. There's a threat in the way you stand, defiance in your eyes. Is it trouble you're here for? If it is, don't worry. There's plenty we can give you.
Aegeus	Tell us now, what is it you want?
Theseus	Speak, before we assume the worst.

The Cretan **Captain** *enters.*

Captain	I'll explain why we're here. I'm captain of this fleet, sent here with express orders from Minos, king of Crete.
Aegeus	Orders? Since when does Crete give Athens orders?
Captain	Since now. Listen to me. Minos sends you this message. He gives you a choice. Either you do as he demands, or he'll send a fleet, much bigger than this, and with it he'll destroy your city.
Theseus	(*Clenching his fists, outraged*) Minos makes demands on us! Threatens us with war! (*Rounding on the Captain*) You can tell your king –
Aegeus	(*To Theseus*) Wait. Let's hear what these demands are.
Captain	(*Calm and businesslike*) I'll be glad to inform you. They're simple. Choose seven youths from among your people. Male or female, either or both will do. Let them say goodbye to their families and friends. Then they'll come on board one of our ships and return with us to Crete. A kind of tribute, if you like. That's the demand. If you agree, all well and good. You won't see us again. (*Threatening*) If not, you will. And, as I said, a bigger fleet next time. Warships. Packed with warriors. We'll burn your city to the ground, slaughter all who live here. (*Pause*) That's the choice. It's yours to make. And make it quickly. We plan to leave today.

Theseus	You don't leave us much time to consider.
Captain	What is there to consider? The choice is plain enough.
Aegeus	Let me ask you one question. Why does Minos want seven of our people?
Captain	That's his business, not yours. I don't have to tell you. But I will. Each spring we hold a great festival. It lasts seven days. Each day one of your people will be dedicated to our gods.
Aegeus	Dedicated?
Captain	Yes. It's a great honour.
Theseus	Speak plainly. They're to be sacrificed.
Captain	If that's the way you want to put it.
Theseus	Now let me ask you a question. Why people from Athens? What have we done to deserve such a great honour?
Captain	Our Cretan gods demand it. They spoke to Minos in a dream.
Theseus	So, seven of our people are to die – throats cut or heads caved in, and all because your king has a dream!
Captain	Not just any dream. A holy dream. You know such dreams can't be ignored. When the gods speak, you listen.
Theseus	We listen to our own gods, not yours.
Captain	You, young man, had best listen to me –
Theseus	Listen to you! An ordinary captain! I am a prince – !
Captain	When I speak, Minos speaks. And Minos is a king, ruler of Crete. And he doesn't quibble with boys.
Theseus	Take this reply from me to your king!

He raises his hand to strike the Captain.

Aegeus	Theseus! No! There'll be no violence!
Captain	(*Calmly*) Best listen to your father, boy. He's wiser than you.
Aegeus	(*To Theseus*) Lower your hand. Do as I say!

> *Theseus lowers his hand and turns away angrily. The Captain speaks to Aegeus.*

Captain	Well, King Aegeus? What's your decision?
Aegeus	How long do I have to give you my reply?
Captain	We sail with the evening tide. I'll wait till then. But if you want my advice, for the good of your people –
Aegeus	I'll decide what's for the good of my people!
Captain	Very well. I'll return to my ships now, and wait there. Till evening.

> *The Captain goes.*
>
> *Theseus turns to Aegeus.*

Theseus	Good thinking, father, to delay them until evening. That gives us five hours. More than enough time to gather an army. They have only three ships, a handful of men in each ship. We'll make short work of them, I promise you. But their captain's to be taken alive. There'll be no quick death for him.
Aegeus	Nor a quick death for any of us, when Minos sends his fleet.
Theseus	Let him! We're more than a match for him and all his ships.
Aegeus	(*He shakes his head, wearily*) But we're not, Theseus. We're no match for him at all. Athens is one city. On Crete there are ninety cities, all bound to Minos. Each city can raise an army to match ours. Can you imagine what will happen when such a force is sent against us? It will be no war. It will be slaughter. Athens will be destroyed.
Theseus	We'll ask for help from other cities – Thebes, Argos, Sparta –

Aegeus	Why should they help us? What's the fate of Athens to them? We stand alone, Theseus. Alone against Minos and the power of Crete. And it will crush us utterly.
Theseus	(*Stubbornly*) Better to die fighting, and with honour, than to crawl like dogs to those Cretans.
Aegeus	Better for you, perhaps. But what about the others who live here? Those who aren't warriors? Old men and women, mothers and their children? Will you condemn those to die because of your honour – and pride?
Theseus	Will you condemn seven to die like slaves in Crete?
Aegeus	Yes – for the sake of the many who will live.
Theseus	(*Realizing*) You've made your decision.
Aegeus	There can't be any other.
Theseus	Then you condemn *me* to die.
Aegeus	What?
Theseus	I shall go as one of the seven.
Aegeus	(*Shocked*) No! You can't!
Theseus	Can I stay here and watch others go to their doom? My honour – my pride won't allow it.
Aegeus	(*Reasoning with his son*) You're prince of Athens – heir to the crown – you have a responsibility –
Theseus	My responsibility is to go where danger threatens, cut my way through to its centre, root it out.
Aegeus	I know you're not afraid of danger. You've proved that often enough. But this – you'll be going to certain death.

Theseus	Perhaps. But once I'm there, who knows? Minos won't send me lightly to my death – a prince of royal blood. And I may find a way to defy him and his gods, and break his power.
Aegeus	You? One man?
Theseus	If not me, then who else?
Aegeus	No – I can't allow it.
Theseus	You've made your decision, father. Now I've made mine. I'm going whether you allow it or not. I'll go to the square, tell the people there what's happening. When they hear I'm going to Crete, there'll be no shortage of those that jump to follow me.

> *Aegeus* and *Theseus* turn from each other, but remain on-stage as the ***Athenian chorus*** speak to the audience, each one leaving as they speak.

Athenian 1	And he's right. There aren't.
Athenian 2	The way he puts it when he tells us, it's like an adventure –
Athenian 3	A great enterprise we'll be setting out on –
Athenian 4	A quest with glory and honour waiting at our journey's end –
Athenian 5	So we volunteer, we six, willing and eager –
Athenian 6	And before the sun's set, we're ready to go.

> *Aegeus* and *Theseus* turn back to face each other. *Aegeus* speaks to Theseus.

Aegeus	Your mind's made up?
Theseus	It is.
Aegeus	Still I can't dissuade you?
Theseus	The others are boarded and waiting for me.

Aegeus   Very well. Go, and take my blessing with you. And promise me
this. Should you return, let the ship you travel in have a white
sail. I'll watch every day from the clifftop for your return. And
when I next see a ship from Crete, I'll know for sure if you're
alive or dead.

Theseus   A white sail. Yes. I'll do that.

Aegeus   You won't forget?

Theseus   I won't forget. You have my word.

> *They embrace, then **Theseus** goes.*
> *The **Cretan chorus** speak to the audience,*
> *each one leaving as they speak.*

Cretan 1   The sun sets and the ships leave the harbour –

Cretan 2   The black ships –

Cretan 3   With the black sails –

Cretan 4   And night falls over the dark sea –

Cretan 5   Wine-dark, blood-dark –

Cretan 6   Carrying its cargo southwards, to Crete.

> ***Aegeus** stands alone. He speaks to the*
> *audience.*

Aegeus   I stood on the headland above the sea and watched them go.
The sun was setting and the sky was deep red, and the waves
red too. A redness in the west turning to dark. The ships black
on the wavetops. The dip and plunge of the oars, the snap of
the sails. They grew smaller as I looked after them, their edges
dissolving into the darkness that gathered about them. Then
the sun sank into the sea and they were gone, and there was
only the black water and the black sky and a cold wind from
the south that whispered among the dry grasses.

> ***Aegeus** goes.*

. . . .

Scene 3

The inner courtyard in Minos' palace.

Androgeus *and* ***Phaedra*** *enter. They look about them, as if to check that there's no one else there, then they go to the centre of the stage. They squat down on the floor.* ***Phaedra*** *bends her head towards the floor, listening.*

Androgeus	Can you hear him?
Phaedra	No.
Androgeus	Let me listen.

*****Androgeus*** *bows his head and listens.*

Androgeus	Nothing. He's not there –
Phaedra	Wait!
Androgeus	What is it?
Phaedra	Ssh!
Androgeus	(*He sits up*) Is he there – ?
Phaedra	(*Interrupting him*) Be quiet!

She listens, intently.

Androgeus	(*Softly*) Can you hear him?
Phaedra	Yes! He's there!
Androgeus	Are you sure?
Phaedra	Listen.

*****Androgeus*** *listens.*

Androgeus	I can hear him! He's down there. Moving about.

They relish imagining the Minotaur's nastiness, capping each other's speeches, increasing in speed.

Phaedra	Shuffling around in the dark.
Androgeus	Snuffling.
Phaedra	Snorting.
Androgeus	It's horrible.
Phaedra	Nasty.
Androgeus	Wicked.
Phaedra	Evil.

*They pause. **Androgeus** sits up and looks at Phaedra.*

Androgeus	Shall we tell him?
Phaedra	That's what we came here for.
Androgeus	Go on, then.
Phaedra	Me?
Androgeus	Yes.
Phaedra	Why not you?
Androgeus	(*An excuse*) He'll hear you better. Your voice is louder.
Phaedra	No, it's not. You're scared of him.
Androgeus	So are you.
Phaedra	Not as scared as you are.

Androgeus	Go on. Tell him.

Phaedra speaks urgently to the Minotaur, beneath the floor.

Phaedra	Brother. Can you hear me? I know you're there. I can hear you. It's me, Phaedra. I've got something to tell you.
Androgeus	Is he listening?
Phaedra	I think so. He's stopped moving.
Androgeus	Perhaps he's gone away.
Phaedra	No. He's there. I can hear him breathing.
Androgeus	Let me speak to him. (*To the Minotaur*) Listen to me, brother, listen! Some people are coming from across the sea.
Phaedra	Far away to the north, and they're coming just for you.

As they talk, they wind each other up and become more and more excited and bloodthirsty.

Androgeus	To be your dinner. Fresh meat.
Phaedra	And when they arrive they'll bring them here.
Androgeus	Send them down to you one by one.
Phaedra	They'll wander around in the dark.
Androgeus	Won't see a thing.
Phaedra	Won't know where they're going.
Androgeus	Till they find you.
Phaedra	Or you find them.
Androgeus	And then – crack!

Phaedra	Smash!
Androgeus	Bite!
Phaedra	Crunch!
Androgeus	You'll eat them up.
Phaedra	Tear their flesh.
Androgeus	Drink their blood.
Phaedra	Chew their bones.
Androgeus	Maybe while they're still alive.
Phaedra	Listen to them screaming.
Androgeus	But you won't care.
Phaedra	Just go on eating.
Androgeus	Because you're a beast.
Phaedra	A brute.
Androgeus	An animal!
Phaedra	A monster.

__Androgeus__ and __Phaedra__ chant together, their voices growing louder.

Androgeus
Phaedra }   Monster! Monster! Monster! Monster! Monster – !

Suddenly, there is a deep, terrifying roar from the ground below. __Phaedra__ and __Androgeus__ cry out and scurry back in fear – colliding with the __Nurse__, who has just entered. They cry out again.

Androgeus   We weren't doing anything!

Phaedra	Don't tell our father!
Androgeus	It was just a bit of fun!

> *Phaedra and Androgeus suddenly remember their social standing. They become haughty and suspicious, rounding on the Nurse and lording it over her.*

Phaedra	What are you doing here anyway?
Nurse	I came –
Androgeus	To spy on us –
Nurse	No –
Phaedra	You're not allowed in here.
Nurse	I know, but –
Androgeus	Perhaps we'll tell our father about you.
Phaedra	How you came in here –
Androgeus	How you upset the monster –
Phaedra	And then he'll send you down there.
Nurse	Listen to me –
Androgeus	(*To Phaedra*) Let's send her down there ourselves.
Phaedra	(*To Androgeus*) Yes! Open the door and push her in.
Androgeus	She can go and say hello to our brother –
Phaedra	And nobody would ever miss her –

> *The Nurse has grown tired of this and shouts at Phaedra and Androgeus.*

Nurse	Stop it! That's enough!

> *Shocked,* **Phaedra** *and* **Androgeus** *fall back.*

Nurse	You two are getting worse! I don't know what's the matter with you, these days! Look at you! I've a good mind to walk out of here now and not tell you the news.

> **Androgeus** *and* **Phaedra** *approach the Nurse again, curious.*

Androgeus	News? What kind of news?
Phaedra	What is it? Tell us.
Androgeus	Please. We're sorry for what we did.
Phaedra	We didn't mean any harm.
Androgeus	Just a bit of fun.
Phaedra	(*Impatient*) What's the news! Tell us the news!
Nurse	All right. The ships have returned from Athens.

> **Phaedra** *and* **Androgeus** *look at her blankly.*

Nurse	From Athens. With the strangers –

> **Androgeus** *and* **Phaedra** *suddenly understand.*

Androgeus	The ships!
Phaedra	The strangers!
Androgeus	They're here!
Phaedra	(*To the Nurse*) Why didn't you tell us straight away?
Androgeus	Let's go and see them!

Phaedra	See if we can guess who they'll send in first!
Androgeus	I'm going to be here when they do!
Phaedra	Me too. I want to listen to his screams!
Androgeus	They'll be horrible!
Phaedra	Blood-chilling!
Androgeus	Loud!
Phaedra	They'll give us nightmares!

Laughing and giggling wickedly,
***Androgeus** and **Phaedra** go, leaving the*
Nurse alone.

Nurse   Like children. Worse than children. I don't know what's got into them. A kind of... madness. And not just them. It seems to me that everyone's got it. And now this bringing of strangers from Athens – and we know for what reason – it makes me shudder to think of it – madness, it is! And who's to blame for it? The king? He's the one who gave out the order. 'Bring them here to feed my son.' For his son must be fed. That one down there, then, he's the one to blame. The poor beast under the ground who hungers for human flesh. But he can't help his appetite, nor what he is. That's god's doing. So there's where the trail of blame ends, with the gods, as it usually does, though I may be damned and blasted for saying it. And what their purpose is, and what will come of it, that we'll never know, till it happens. And it's probably best that we don't.

*The **Nurse** goes.*

• •

Scene 4

The harbour at Knossos, later that day.

*The Cretan **Captain** enters, leading on the **Athenian chorus** and **Theseus**. They stand central. The **Captain** speaks to them.*

Captain Here we are at last. Your journey's done. There's the road that leads to Knossos, and there you can see the city itself. Grander than your own, you'll have to admit. You'll go there later. For now, wait here on the harbour-side. King Minos is coming to greet you – and to tell you what your fate will be.

*The **Captain** stands aside, as the **Cretan chorus** enter, gazing with curiosity at the Athenian chorus, and talking excitedly among themselves.*

Cretan 1 Look! They're here! The strangers from Athens!

Cretan 2 From across the sea, another country!

Cretan 3 Foreigners, northerners – not at all like us!

Cretan 4 How strange they look – their clothes! their faces!

Cretan 5 Savages, really – nothing refined about them!

Cretan 6 But proud – the way they carry themselves!

*The **Cretan chorus** direct their attention to Theseus.*

Cretan 1 And that one there – even more proud than the others!

Cretan 2 He must be their leader – he has a look about him!

Cretan 3 Something fierce in his gaze! Fierce and fearless!

Cretan 4 The way he looks at us – as if we were *his* prisoners!

Cretan 5 That won't last long – when he finds out what's in store.

| Cretan 6 | He'll have a new look, then – fear and terror! |

Theseus speaks to the Athenian chorus.

| Theseus | Stand firm. Hold your heads up. Don't stir or speak. Even if you're afraid, don't let them see it. Barbarians – that's what they are – nothing to make us tremble. And if you do feel yourself start to shiver a little, tell yourself it's just the breeze coming in off the ocean. And remember who you are – Athenians, Greeks, and there's no one better. |

*The **Athenian chorus** speak to the audience.*

Athenian 1	We hear his words, try to hold them in our hearts –
Athenian 2	But it's not easy – words don't seem to mean much here.
Athenian 3	We can't help wishing we hadn't come here now –
Athenian 4	We shouldn't have been so eager to volunteer.
Athenian 5	His words back then filled us with thoughts of glory –
Athenian 6	Now there's only the salt-taste of fear –
Athenian 1	As we look at the crowds gathered about us –
Athenian 2	Pushing and shoving, trying to catch a glimpse –
Athenian 3	And their cries are frenzied, and there's hunger in their eyes –
Athenian 4	And there's music and acrobats, jugglers and tumblers –
Athenian 5	The whole place is like some madhouse carnival –
Athenian 6	A lunatic circus – a festival of fools.

*The **Cretan chorus** chant.*

| Cretans | Minos! Minos! Minos! Minos! |

*Their chanting grows louder and more
frenzied, building to a climax as **Minos**
himself enters, dressed richly and grandly.
On his entrance, **Minos** holds up a hand,
and the **Cretan chorus** fall silent. He
turns to the Athenians and addresses them.
As he speaks, he grows more and agitated.*

Minos   Welcome, dear guests, to the land of Crete. Your coming here
is an honour to us, an honour to our gods – and an honour
indeed to yourselves. What you see here is the beginning of
our great yearly festival – the festival at which we celebrate the
birth of god, his resurrection and return to life, springing
forth, renewed, from the dark earth that has held him – reborn
in all his might and power and glory. And you, my Athenian
friends, have been brought here to partake in this rite and
celebration. (*Getting more excited*) For you must know that our
god, unlike others, is no god of air and spirit! Here, on Crete,
god has descended to earth, has taken the form of flesh and
blood, and sleeps now in the dark beneath us. And to you will
fall the great and glorious task of awakening this god.
(*Relishing the thought*) Each in turn shall descend into earth's
deep, and with your flesh and blood shall give him strength to
stir, and upon the seventh day, to rise once more. To stamp his
feet, to bellow, to roar! (*Now very agitated*) And with his rising
he shall renew the life of Crete, in which your spirits, freed
from the bonds of flesh, shall dwell eternal!

*He pauses, calms himself, turns and speaks
to the Captain.*

Minos   Bring them to the city. Tonight they'll sleep there, as our
honoured guests. And tomorrow we'll see which one shall be
first to face the god.

***Minos** goes. The **Captain** approaches the
Athenian chorus and Theseus.*

Captain   You heard. We take the road to Knossos. A road, for you, that
leads only one way.

Theseus   Perhaps. Whether we return or not remains to be seen.

Captain	Brave words. I hope to hear you speak them tomorrow. Follow me.

> *The **Captain** goes, followed by the **Athenian chorus** and **Theseus**.*
>
> *The **Cretan chorus** speak to the audience, each one leaving as they speak.*

Cretan 1	We follow too, take the long road back –
Cretan 2	And though there's still laughter, noise and music –
Cretan 3	Though the masks and the costumes are bright in the sunlight –
Cretan 4	We fear what we'll come to when the revels are ended –
Cretan 5	What we'll hear in the silence when the singing's over –
Cretan 6	What we'll see in the mirror when the masks are off.

> *The stage is empty.*

• •

Scene 5

The inner courtyard in Minos' palace, the same day.

***Daedalus** enters. He speaks aloud to himself.*

Daedalus   It's plain he's mad. Of course, I always knew he was... unbalanced. Neurotic. Even, at times, a little deranged. But now – that beast under the ground is god's son! And he himself, therefore, must be god! It's obvious he's gone completely insane. A madman on the throne of Crete – and a dangerous one. Those seven from Athens won't be the last to feed his madness. The more it's fed, the hungrier it will become. And he can't always send abroad for his fodder. The last time we spoke together, he looked at me – and what I saw in his eyes I didn't like. I should have realized then... (*He looks down towards the door in the floor*) It'll be a special treat for you to find me down there, won't it, Asterius? The one who built your prison for you, caught in his own trap. The tormentor destroyed by the tormented. No, you won't have that pleasure. If there's to be a death, it must be yours, not mine. Kill you, and cure the king's madness. But how to bring that about? I'm no hero. And where in Crete is such a man to be found?

***Ariadne** has entered during the above, un-noticed by Daedalus. She has the knife and the thread concealed on her. She speaks to Daedalus. She is cold, hard, aloof, and shows her dislike of him.*

Ariadne   I think I know of one.

***Daedalus** turns quickly, startled at seeing Ariadne.*

Daedalus   Ariadne –

Ariadne   A man who may bring an end to this madness. Destroy the monster, set Crete free of its tyranny. That's what you're talking about, isn't it? Finding someone who'll kill my poor brother. Don't pretend otherwise. There's no time for

	pretence. We must speak plainly. You want to save your skin. I want to bring an end to my brother's misery. They both mean the same thing. Killing him.
Daedalus	Very well. Plain speaking it is. If we're all to be saved from this insanity, the monster – your brother must die. But it will take no ordinary man to slay him. You said you knew of someone.
Ariadne	I do. At least, if anyone is the man, I think it's him.
Daedalus	Who is it?
Ariadne	One of the strangers who came today.
Daedalus	An Athenian?
Ariadne	Yes. Their leader.
Daedalus	What makes you think he could do... do this deed?
Ariadne	I was at the harbour when they arrived – I saw how they stood amidst all the noise and shouting – calm, silent, dignified. And I saw him. Their leader. There was something special about him. A light, that seemed to shine around him – a strength within – as if he'd been truly touched by god. And I knew I saw a man who was without fear – a man whom nothing could ever harm or hurt.
Daedalus	A hero.
Ariadne	Yes.
Daedalus	And you'll offer this hero your help. Which of course he'll accept.
Ariadne	He won't go into the labyrinth unarmed.
Daedalus	Going in is easy. Getting out again's a different matter. Which is where, I presume, my help's needed. Unless, of course, he's just left in there –

Ariadne	Leave a man to wander in the dark until he dies? That may be your way, Daedalus, but it's not mine! You'll help him find a way out.
Daedalus	I bow to your wishes, Princess Ariadne. But it's no easy matter. I'll have to give it some thought. Some deep thought. We'll speak again later.

He makes a move to go.

Ariadne	Before night.
Daedalus	Indeed. Of course. Before night.

***Daedalus** goes.*

***Ariadne** speaks sadly to her brother, in the labyrinth beneath the floor.*

Ariadne	My poor brother. Do you know what you've become? Kept in the dark, starved, half-crazed with hunger. A beast they called you, and a beast is what they've made you. Do you understand? And would you understand if you knew what I'm doing now? I think the madness must have touched me too. I'm plotting your death, the only one who ever cared for you. The only one who cares for you now. Because it's the only way to free you from your torment and your prison – and free me from mine. Crete. A prison and a torment to us both. Your death. It must be. It's all that I can do for you now. All that can be done.

She remains on-stage.

· ·

Scene 6

The inner courtyard, next day.

*The **Cretan chorus** enter and speak to the audience.*

Cretan 1	And this is what was done.

Cretan 2	Last night, while all were sleeping –
Cretan 3	Ariadne went secretly to see Theseus.
Cretan 4	She told him of the beast that lay in the labyrinth –
Cretan 5	That this beast was no god, but her monstrous brother –
Cretan 6	And that she, the beast's sister, would help him destroy it.

Theseus enters to Ariadne. She turns to
face him and they speak together.

Theseus	You? Minos' daughter? Why?
Ariadne	I hate the tyrant my father's become – and pity that beast that's my brother.
Theseus	(*Not understanding*) You pity him, but want me to kill him?
Ariadne	He lives in torment. It's the only escape for him – and for me.
Theseus	Escape for you?
Ariadne	After you've killed him – if you kill him – you'll flee from here, return to Athens. When you do, I want you to take me with you. That's my price for helping you.
Theseus	It's fair. I agree. You'll come with me to Athens. Now tell me. How do you propose to help me?
Ariadne	They intend to send you unarmed into the labyrinth – easy prey for my brother. But you won't go unarmed. (*She takes out the knife*) Take this knife. Kill my brother with it. A single blow if you can.

Theseus takes the knife from Ariadne.

Theseus	A single blow. I'll do my best.

Ariadne	If you do – if you succeed in killing him, the danger won't be over. The labyrinth has been made in such a way that none who enter can find a way out. You'll be lost among its winding passages, wander there until you die. That's the intention.
Theseus	But you know a way I can escape?
Ariadne	Yes. The man who built it told me the means. (*She takes out the ball of thread*) Take this ball of thread. Unwind it as you walk through the passages. Then, when you've... killed my brother, follow the thread and it will lead you back.

Theseus takes the thread.

Theseus	(*Smirking*) A knife and a ball of thread. A hero's weapons.

Ariadne	They're all the weapons you have – and all you'll need.
Theseus	It's true. I've faced dangers with less than these – and survived.
Ariadne	If you survive this, remember our bargain. Take me with you to Athens.
Theseus	I'll remember.
Ariadne	Give me your word on it.
Theseus	You have my word.

Ariadne	If you break it, you'll be cursed. Your whole life blighted. And not just you – all of your blood. Remember those words – and see to it they never come to pass.

> *Ariadne turns and goes. The **Cretan** chorus speak.*

Cretan 1	Then she was gone.
Cretan 2	Theseus waited alone –
Cretan 3	For the sun to rise, the day to come.
Cretan 4	And now his waiting's over.
Cretan 5	The sun's risen.
Cretan 6	The day has come.

> *Minos enters and speaks to Theseus. Although his words are sane, the delivery of these lines, and the way Minos behaves, should indicate his insanity – without going over the top.*

Minos	You're to be the first to meet with the god?
Theseus	I am.
Minos	Were you elected, or did you choose the honour?
Theseus	I chose, freely. It was I led the others here. It was my words persuaded them to come. It's right and just, therefore, that I go first into the dark. I'm their captain and their prince. I'm Theseus, son of King Aegeus.

> *Minos is taken aback by this.*

Minos	The king's son? And you came here as a slave?
Theseus	Not as a slave. As a free man. I'll face this beast of yours as a free man. And, if the god wills it, as a free man I'll die.

Minos	He wills it. You can be sure of that. He waits for you, now, in the dark earth. He hungers for you. And you shall feed that hunger. A king's son! Royal blood for the god to drink! It's fitting. As you said yourself, right and just. Theseus, prince of Athens, for this brave deed your name will live forever. Though I fear *you* shall not.

Minos goes.

Theseus speaks to the audience.

Theseus	I'm ready. The time's come. Let me enter the labyrinth.

Theseus crosses to one side of the stage and waits there.

. . . .

Scene 7

Inside the labyrinth.

The **Athenian chorus** *enter. They and the* **Cretan chorus** *both speak now. As they do, they take up positions on the centre stage, creating a maze-like pattern, representing the labyrinth.* **Theseus** *walks among them, as if threading his way through the winding passageways.*

Athenian 1	He enters the doorway –
Athenian 2	Descends the dark stairway –
Athenian 3	And darkness enfolds him –
Athenian 4	Like a living creature –
Athenian 5	Wrapping its tentacles around him –
Athenian 6	Dragging him down, deeper and deeper –
Cretan 1	Through winding passageways –

Cretan 2	Turning and twisting –
Cretan 3	Like the coils of a snake –
Cretan 4	Writhing in darkness –
Cretan 5	Digesting him into its darkness –
Cretan 6	Where dreams die black in the bedrock horror.

> *Theseus* has now come to the centre of the labyrinth, with the chorus around him. *Asterius* comes on, hidden behind the chorus. *Theseus* speaks to the audience.

Theseus   Suddenly there's light. A single shaft of pale light coming down from far above. Facing me is a chamber hollowed out of the rock. The passage I'm standing in leads to the chamber. There's no other entrance. And I know that I've come to the centre of the labyrinth.

> The *Chorus* begin to move away from Theseus as they speak.

Athenian 1	A smell of decay –
Cretan 1	Air close and hot –
Athenian 2	Bones on the floor –
Cretan 2	Rags of skin, dried blood –
Athenian 3	Grim trophies hung from the walls –
Cretan 3	Feathers, claws –
Athenian 4	Scalps of human hair –
Cretan 4	And a deep breathing –
Athenian 5	Some creature moving –
Cretan 5	Shuffling out of the dark –

Athenian 6   A knot of the dark, given form, shape –

Cretan 6   Horned, monstrous, the shape of the beast.

> *As the **Chorus** finally part, Asterius is revealed, standing central, facing Theseus. **Theseus** speaks, keeping his eyes fixed on Asterius.*

Theseus   It comes forward, stands before me, its bulk blocking the entrance. Part-man, part-beast. More terrible than I'd ever imagined. And most terrible of all, its eyes – human eyes gazing out of an animal face. And its voice when it speaks is human too.

> *Asterius speaks to Theseus.*

Asterius   Welcome, man. This is my home. The bottom of the world. These are the last paths your feet will walk. (*He points upwards*) That light is the last light you will see. You have come here to die.

> *Theseus speaks to Asterius.*

Theseus   To die? No. I have come here to kill.

Asterius   Kill me? You do not have the power or strength.

Theseus   Perhaps not. But I have this.

> *Theseus raises the knife.*

Asterius   That blade will not harm me.

Theseus   We'll see about that. No more talking. Let's fight.

Asterius   To the death.

Theseus   To the death.

> *Asterius now narrates, as he and Theseus fight. The fight may be stylized, performed in slow-motion.*

Asterius	I watch him, this man. I see how he moves. How he watches me. Looking for the chance, the right moment. It comes! He strikes! I fling him away. But he does not fall. He watches again. Strikes again! Again I fling him away. Again! And again! But always he returns. And now I fear him. I fear this man. His eyes, watching me. Not human eyes. The eyes of an animal staring from a human face.

Theseus speaks to Asterius.

Theseus	You still think I'm not the man to kill you?
Asterius	No man can kill me. I am a god.
Theseus	You're no god. And you're nothing human. You're a monster, a beast.
Asterius	A beast, then. A beast that will feast on your flesh.
Theseus	Your days of feasting are finished.
Asterius	Why deceive yourself, man? Your death is certain. You can never escape from here. Even if you do kill me, you will wander in the dark until you die.
Theseus	That's not the case. I know a way out.
Asterius	How can you know?
Theseus	I was given help.
Asterius	Who would help you?
Theseus	Ariadne.
Asterius	(*He starts at the name, betrayed*) Ariadne? My sister.
Theseus	She wants you dead. Her brother who is no brother. A beast. A monster. A thing of horror. She wants me to kill you. And so I shall.

Asterius pauses for a moment. Then he speaks, softly.

Asterius	And so you shall.

> *Asterius kneels down. He does not move as Theseus narrates his own actions.*

Theseus It kneels before me, accepting its death. Remains still as I approach it. Looks outward, beyond me, as if it doesn't see me. There's something shining on its face. Wet. It's tears. Tears on the beast's face. But I have no pity. I move around the creature, stand behind it, push it to the floor. It falls without a sound. Then I grasp its hair, pull its head up and back, raise my knife, and cut its throat.

> *Asterius is facing out, Theseus standing behind him. Theseus draws his knife across Asterius' throat. Off-stage, a loud roaring sound. Theseus pushes Asterius forward. Asterius falls face down. Theseus rips off the bull-mask and holds it up, triumphantly. The roaring fades to silence.*

> *Ariadne enters. She walks up to Theseus.*

Ariadne It's done?

Theseus Yes.

> *Ariadne takes the mask from him. For a moment she holds it, tenderly, then places it on the floor beside the body of Asterius.*

Ariadne We must go, then.

Theseus Is it safe?

Ariadne Yes. Everyone's sleeping.

Theseus And there's a ship?

Ariadne As I promised, in the harbour.

Theseus And my companions?

Ariadne	Waiting there for us. Quickly, now. Hurry.

Theseus and Ariadne go.

*The **Athenian chorus** speak, each one leaving as they speak.*

Athenian 1	In the dead of night we board the ship –
Athenian 2	Raise the anchor, cast off from the quayside –
Athenian 3	Take to the oars and row out of the harbour –
Athenian 4	Haul on the ropes, hoist up the sail –
Athenian 5	Let the wind fill it, driving us onward –
Athenian 6	Away from Crete, to the open sea.

*The first three **Cretans** leave as they speak.*

Cretan 1	And with the sun's rising, Crete wakes to the news –
Cretan 2	The beast is killed and the strangers have fled –
Cretan 3	And the princess is gone and Minos is raving –

Cretan 4 takes Asterius' mask off-stage while speaking.

Cretan 4	And the people are out and it looks like trouble –

*The last two **Cretans** drag off Asterius' body as they speak.*

Cretan 5	Crowds in the streets, rioting, looting –
Cretan 6	It looks like everything's falling apart.

They go with the body.

. . . .

Scene 8

The palace of Minos, the same morning.

Androgeus *runs on-stage, followed by the* ***Nurse***.

Androgeus	I won't go! I won't!
Nurse	You must –
Androgeus	No –
Nurse	Your father says –
Androgeus	It doesn't matter what he says. He's mad.
Nurse	That's a terrible thing to say.
Androgeus	It's true, though.
Nurse	We'll have no more talk like that. Now, come along –
Androgeus	No! You can't make me!
Nurse	But it's not safe here!
Androgeus	This is the royal palace! Of course it's safe!
Nurse	Not any more. Can't you hear them? That crowd outside? They're at the doors. It won't be long before they break them down.
Androgeus	They won't dare!
Nurse	They'll dare anything today. Gone completely wild, they have.
Androgeus	Where are the soldiers? Why aren't they dealing with them?
Nurse	The soldiers are with them! You must go! Your father has a ship waiting –
Androgeus	I've told you I won't go! Not without *him*!

Nurse	Without who?
Androgeus	He must be here somewhere.
Nurse	Who? Who are you talking about?
Androgeus	Achilles, you stupid old woman! I'm not going without Achilles!

Phaedra has entered, with the puppet.

Phaedra	(*To the Nurse*) He means this. His puppet.
Androgeus	You found him!

Androgeus snatches the puppet off Phaedra, and puts it on his hand.

Androgeus	Now we can fight them all! Achilles and I, we'll stand together, we'll beat them back –
Phaedra	(*To Androgeus*) You idiot! What are you two going to do against that mob? A puppet and an idiot! They've got weapons! The city's burning! We've got to go.
Androgeus	I don't want to! This is my home!
Phaedra	All right, then. Stay! I really don't care!

Phaedra turns as if to go.

Androgeus	Phaedra! Don't leave me! I'm scared!
Phaedra	(*Turning back*) Come on, then.
Androgeus	What about Ariadne? Isn't she coming?
Phaedra	You are such an idiot, aren't you? Ariadne's gone! She ran away to Athens! She helped the stranger kill our brother. All this is her fault.
Nurse	You can't be sure of that –

Phaedra	Yes I can. Daedalus told everything. After he'd been tortured. And now he's locked up in his own labyrinth.
Androgeus	Is he? Is he in there?
Phaedra	Yes.
Androgeus	Good. Serves him right. I never liked him.

> *A drumming sound starts in the background. The* **Nurse** *starts.*

Nurse	Listen! They're beating the doors down! You'd better go! There isn't much time!
Phaedra	Aren't you coming?
Nurse	I'll follow you. Go on, go on! Hurry!

> **Phaedra** *and* **Androgeus** *go. The* **Nurse** *speaks calmly to the audience.*

Nurse	I shan't follow. I've done with them. Not that I want to see them harmed, but I've given that family enough years of service, and all for no thanks. Good riddance to them, I say. Now I'll go to the doors and let the mob in. Join them, ransack the palace. And help myself to a share of the loot.

> *The* **Nurse** *goes.*

· ·

Scene 9

> *The return journey – the Aegean sea and sky, the island of Naxos, Athens.*
>
> **Theseus** *enters and speaks to the audience.*

Theseus	There's a fair wind blowing from the south, the sky's clear, the sea's calm. No thundercloud covers the sun, no storm whips up the waves to bring us trouble. As if some god is with us,

watching over us. Heaven itself has blessed our enterprise. And as I lift my face towards the sky, I see the sign of that blessing.

*The **Athenian chorus** enter as they speak.*

Athenian 1	We see it too –
Athenian 2	A miracle –
Athenian 3	A wonder –
Athenian 4	Soaring above us –
Athenian 5	A messenger from heaven –
Athenian 6	A winged figure flying out of the sun.

***Daedalus** enters on another part of the stage and speaks to the audience.*

Daedalus   No god's messenger, no sign from heaven. But a wonder certainly. Not least to myself. I escaped from the labyrinth. I'd built a secret passage that led up to the clifftops above the sea. Once there, I constructed my true masterpiece. Feathers, wood, wax. Where Talos failed, I succeeded. I spread my arms wide, and stepped off into space. The wind took me, lifted me up, above the earth, above the sea, out of this story and out of this world, to a destination no man knows.

***Daedalus** goes.*

*On the other side of the stage, **Ariadne** enters and speaks to the audience.*

Ariadne   I saw him too, as I stood alone on the shore of the island. I knew it was him. I held in my hands the winged figure he'd made for me. And I raised it up, and in grief and rage, flung it into the air. It rose, shining, flashing in the sunlight – then turned and fell, and dropped into the waves. And now I stand alone at the sea's edge, and I weep bitter tears, and I curse the man who abandoned me here.

*The **Athenian chorus** speak to the
audience, clearly on Theseus' side.*

Athenian 1   Theseus isn't to blame. He had to do it.

Athenian 2   He was forced to leave the girl there.

Athenian 3   We put in at this island, Naxos, they call it –

Athenian 4   Put in there for fresh water and food –

Athenian 5   It was a hot day and the work made us drowsy –

Athenian 6   And after we'd loaded the ship, we slept.

Theseus   And as I slept a god appeared to me. Wooden staff in his
hand, vine-leaves in his hair, a leopard at his side – Dionysus,
god of wine. This was his island, he told me, and he wanted a
gift. Ariadne. He wanted her to be his bride. He'd put her into

an enchanted sleep. She wouldn't wake until we'd gone. I must leave her there, he told me – leave her to him or endure his wrath. And though it grieved me, that's what I did. There was no choice. The god had spoken.

Ariadne   That's what he says. That's what he'll tell everyone. But he lies! He lies in his teeth and the truth is this! He never intended to take me to Athens. Used me, and then discarded me, abandoned me here, a piece of flotsam. I know I shall die here, and I'll die cursing him. I send my curse to him now, screaming like a seabird across the waves. A curse to blight his life, him and all his blood!

Ariadne goes.

Athenian 1   We sail on, speeding towards Athens –

Athenian 2   The wind in our hair, the salt-spray on our faces –

Athenian 3   The sunlight flashing like bright laughter from the waves.

Athenian 4   Then the smell of earth, seabirds circling –

Athenian 5   A dark shape rising out of the sea –

Athenian 6   The cliffs of our own country, the headlands of home.

*On another part of the stage, **Aegeus** enters and stands centre stage.*

Aegeus   (*To the audience*) I stood on that headland, where I'd stood each day, looking out for my son's return. And, as on the day of his leaving, a cold wind blew, a cold voice whispered. I shivered. Suddenly I felt old. Then I saw the ship coming over the horizon, watched eagerly as it approached from the south. A black ship – with a black sail. Then I knew my son was dead. Despair seized me. (*He takes off his crown and throws it on the stage*) I stepped off the headland into empty air, and fell to my death on the rocks below, and now my bones lie white on the sea's bed.

Aegeus goes.

> *On the other side of the stage, Aethra enters*
> *and speaks to the audience.*

Aethra   So the words of the goddess were fulfilled at last. And at last I
                      had my longed-for revenge.

> *Aethra goes to Theseus, takes his hand,*
> *and leads him to the centre, where she picks*
> *up the crown and ceremoniously places it on*
> *his head. As she does this, the **Athenian***
> ***chorus** speak.*

Athenian 1   It wasn't his fault. You can't blame him –

Athenian 2   He was sleeping as we approached land –

Athenian 3   And we didn't know about his promise.

Athenian 4   By the time he woke, it was too late –

Athenian 5   And he entered the city to the bad news –

Athenian 6   And a hero's welcome, and the crown of Athens.

> *Theseus makes a speech to the audience.*
> *He begins with sadness in his voice, but this*
> *gradually gives way to triumph.*

Theseus   Citizens of Athens, you offer me this crown and I accept it.
                      But in accepting, I grieve for the death of my father. And, so
                      that his name shall never be forgotten, the sea which took his
                      life shall bear his name for all time. In that name too, I'll rule
                      as well and wisely as I'm able, and pray we'll know prosperity
                      and peace. (*Gaining more confidence*) For Athens has no
                      enemies left now. The monster of Crete has been destroyed,
                      Minos overthrown, his power broken. (*Triumphantly*) There's
                      nothing to prevent our city from rising to true greatness –
                      wealthy, powerful, a place of justice and just living – a haven
                      and harbour to citizens and strangers, a shining beacon of
                      glory throughout the known world.

> *The **Athenian chorus** cheer and call out.*
> *As they do, the **Cretan chorus** enter in a*

close-packed group, with **Asterius** *hidden behind them. When the cheering dies down, they speak.*

Cretan 1	But even as the people cheered –
Cretan 2	Even as they called out their new king's name –
Cretan 3	At that moment of celebration and victory –
Cretan 4	A shadow fell across the city –
Cretan 5	A shadow from the south –
Cretan 6	Horned, black, the shadow of the bull.

Asterius moves out from behind the Cretan chorus, and speaks to Theseus.

Asterius   My shadow shall haunt you all your days, called from the grave by my sister's curse. A shadow that lies in your heart, and the hearts of all men, your doom and your fate, the bane of your blood and all your kind.

Athenian 1   So it was. So it shall be. He'll make Athens great, bring law and peace to all the country around –

Cretan 1   Have a son, Hippolytus, by a foreign queen. A son whom he worships and adores.

Athenian 2   He'll marry Ariadne's sister, Phaedra, and so unite Athens and Crete –

Cretan 2   But then Phaedra will fall in love with his son. And when he rejects her, she'll accuse him of rape.

Athenian 3   Fearing for his life, Hippolytus will flee, and Theseus, in his rage, will call on the gods –

Cretan 3   And the gods will hear him, and send a bull from the sea, and Hippolytus will go down to his doom.

Athenian 4	Phaedra, his wife, will hang herself. In grief at these deaths, Theseus will go mad –
Cretan 4	He'll become a tyrant. His people will fear him. Even his own mother will turn against him.
Athenian 5	Fear will become anger. They'll take the crown from him, turn him out of the city, banish him forever.
Cretan 5	Outcast, alone, he'll wander the world, tramping its trackways, a beggar on the road –
Athenian 6	And at last, in some remote place, he'll be set upon by bandits, beaten, murdered –
Cretan 6	And his body thrown in some deep pit. And no one shall know where his bones lie.

*All, except Theseus and Asterius, turn and go. When they have gone, **Asterius** speaks.*

Asterius   Once there was a king.

*Asterius takes the crown from Theseus' head, raises it up, then lowers it and places it on the floor. **Theseus** and **Asterius** turn and go off opposite sides of the stage.*

All that remains is the crown, central.

· ·

Activities

Theseus and the Minotaur

Theseus – the Hero?

Theseus is only one of many Greek heroes – others include
Odysseus, Jason, Heracles (also known as Hercules), and Perseus.
Many of these Greek heroes were the children of Zeus, king of the
gods, by human women: in fact, the Greek definition of a hero was
more or less someone who had a god or goddess for one of their
parents.

Theseus and the
Minotaur: a mosaic
floor from a Roman
villa near Salzburg

Heroes today are rather different – but in what ways?

*Research and
Discuss*

1 Start by comparing the qualities of Greek and modern-day heroes,
using a table like the one below. The list for Greek heroes has been
done for you. What makes a modern-day hero? Think of heroes in
books, in films, people who are hailed as 'heroes' by the media... Fill in
the chart with your findings.

Greek hero	Modern-day hero
Has a god for a parent	
Goes on great voyages or quests	
Kills monsters	

2 Now think about Theseus in the play. Which is he more like: a modern hero or an ancient Greek one? Think about some of the things he does in the play. In your opinion, is he a hero?

Theseus – the Game

Read and Design

Look again at Act 2, Scene 1, where Theseus meets the bandits on the road to Athens, and at Act 3, Scenes 6 and 7, in which Theseus meets and kills the Minotaur. Then, in a group, imagine that you are working for a company that produces computer games. You have been asked to draw up the details of a game based on Theseus' exploits, and to set up the marketing campaign for it.

1 As a whole group, decide what the game will be like:
   - the different levels in the game, and what will happen in each (e.g. the first level might involve Theseus finding the sword; the last level might be the final battle with the Minotaur)
   - what Theseus' strengths and weaknesses are
   - who the game will be aimed at – your 'target market'.
   Make notes on your discussions.
2 Then divide up the group. You will work on different parts of the project, using the notes you have just made. (If there are enough of you in your group you can work in pairs.) The different areas are:
   - writing a report to the game designers on how the game will work
   - writing a brief for the artists on what the characters should look like
   - writing advertising copy for a magazine advertisement which you will use to attract customers – decide what information they will need about the game (price? where to buy it?) and include a really good slogan to get people interested.

The Final Battle

Read and Write

1 Re-read Act 3, Scene 7, where Theseus finally meets and fights the Minotaur.
2 Plan an extract from an adventure story, describing the fight. Before you start writing, think about different stages in the fight: should Theseus be winning all the time? You will want to build up some tension to keep your reader gripped. Remember that this sort of account concentrates on action, and there should be plenty of it.

3 Now write your story. You could start like this:

> As Theseus felt his way through the dark labyrinth, he could hear the monster's howl coming nearer and nearer. He gripped his sword, ready to fight to the death.

Read All About It!

Write

At the end of the play, Theseus is king of Athens. Imagine you are a reporter for an Athens newspaper. You have to write a report of the coronation.

You could quote parts of Theseus' speech on page 100. How do you think the people of Athens would react to it, and to him as king? Include this in your report.

You will also want to include some of the key facts from Theseus's past, in a mini-biography. Which parts of Theseus' story will you include?

Think of
- headlines and subheadings
- pictures you could use to illustrate your article.

If you can, lay out the finished piece as a real newspaper article.

Asterius, the Minotaur

In the original legend, the Minotaur does not have a name and is not treated as a person. It is a monster pure and simple, hidden away in the labyrinth, thirsting for human flesh. Theseus decides to kill it because this is the only way to stop the sacrifices. Ariadne falls in love with Theseus, and this is the only reason why she helps him.

In the play, the portrayal of the Minotaur is quite different. For a start, he has a name and we see him before he is shut up in the labyrinth.

Read and Discuss   1 Look at what Ariadne says about Asterius' imprisonment and its effect
                       on him, at the bottom of page 60. Does she think Asterius is a monster?
                     2 Now look at the other speeches and hints about Asterius' character,
                       both in what he says and in what other characters say about him.
                       (Remember that some of the characters are more sympathetic to him
                       than others.) Gather evidence about him: does he become a monster,
                       as Ariadne suggests, or is he born one? Here are some of the things you
                       could look at:
                       • what Phaedra and Androgeus say about him (pages 51–53)
                       • how he reacts to Phaedra and Androgeus (pages 53–54)
                       • how he behaves with Ariadne (pages 54–56)
                       • what Ariadne says about him when she has decided to betray him
                         (page 84).
                     3 Now look at the scene where Theseus meets Asterius (pages 90–92).
                       How does Theseus describe him at first sight? How does Asterius react
                       to the news of Ariadne's betrayal?
                     4 Has Asterius become a monster through the play, as Ariadne thought
                       he would?

A ceremonial wine-jar
in the shape of a bull's
head, found in the
ruins of the palace
at Knossos, Crete

Theseus and the Minotaur

Debate

In the play, which one of these two characters is the monster?

Is the Minotaur evil, or a victim? And what about Theseus? He performs brave acts – but can also be cruel and selfish.

Divide the class into two groups for a debate. One group will argue that Theseus is more of a monster than Asterius. The other will argue that Asterius is really the monster.

1 Look at the play together, especially the scenes you have looked at for the activities on page 107. Gather evidence in a grid to support your group's point of view. One group will look for evidence that Theseus is good and Asterius bad; the other will look for evidence that Theseus is bad and Asterius good.

2 Use the evidence in your grid to prepare your arguments for the debate.

3 Hold the debate, with the teacher as chair. At the end of the debate, vote: who is more of a monster?

The Other Main Characters

Ariadne

Like Asterius, Ariadne is a more complicated character in the play than in the original legend.

Women in Greek myths are often even more two-dimensional than the men – women in Greek society had few rights and little choice about what they did with their lives. David Calcutt's version of Ariadne is more like a modern woman than one in a Greek legend.

Hot Seat

1 To explore Ariadne as a character, read three key scenes from the play in which she is involved:
  - when Daedalus arrives and gives gifts to her, Phaedra and Androgeus (pages 27–30)
  - when Asterius is trapped in the labyrinth (pages 58–60)
  - after Minos speaks to the Athenian prisoners (page 80).
2 For each scene, think of some questions to ask Ariadne. For example, how does she feel about her family in the first scene? What does she think will happen next after Asterius has been tricked into the labyrinth? What does she think of Crete in the third scene?
3 Choose three different people to take the hot seat as Ariadne, one for each scene. Ask your questions.
4 What do you think of the answers?
5 Based on the research you have done, and the questions and answers in the hot seating activity, choose one of the scenes and imagine that you are Ariadne. Write your diary for the day when that scene took place: what happened? How did it make you feel?
You could start:

Today has been another extraordinary day and nothing will ever be the same again.

Daedalus

Daedalus in the play is more than a simple craftsman. As well as
designing and building the labyrinth, he proves to be very good at
manipulating people:

- He persuades Minos to take him on.
- He fools Ariadne into helping him trap Asterius in the labyrinth
  (Act 2, Scene 2).
- He switches sides at the right point and decides to help Ariadne
  (Act 3, Scene 5).

Note and Discuss   1 Look again at Act 1, Scene 3, and Act 2, Scene 2. In these scenes, a
range of characters – Minos, the Cretan courtiers, Minos' children, the
Nurse, Asterius – reveal their thoughts and feelings about Daedalus,
either through their speech or through their behaviour.
For each of these characters, make notes on:
a what they thought of Daedalus when they first met him
b what they thought of him afterwards.
Try to find evidence from the play for each answer.

2 What do you think of Daedalus? In pairs or groups, discuss your view
of him. Do you admire him, or dislike him? Do you think he deserves
to escape at the end of the play?

Daedalus and Talos

Storyboard   Before Daedalus came to Crete, he was accused of murder in Athens.
Look at the scene where he tells Minos and the courtiers about what
happened (pages 30–36).

Imagine you are filming the scene. In groups, draw up a storyboard
to show how this scene will be shot.

1 As a class, start by dividing the scene into sections, e.g.
a Beginning of scene: Minos' court
b Flashback: Daedalus' flight from Athens
c Minos' court
d Flashback: Daedalus' version of events
e Flashback: the court in Athens
f Talos' version of events
g Minos' court (to end of scene).

2 Then split the class into groups. Each group takes a section of the
scene, and draws a storyboard to indicate how they would film that
section. Each frame of the storyboard should show what would appear
on screen. (You don't have to be good at drawing – stick figures will

do.) Underneath each frame, write the key lines of dialogue which will accompany the action. Remember that you can use close-ups on characters' faces when you want to see their emotions; longer shots when you want to show action or set the scene.

3 Finally, display the storyboards around the class in the right order, so that you can 'see' the whole scene from beginning to end.

Minos

King Minos in legend was a great law-giver, a wise ruler who controlled a vast empire. Like many Greek heroes, he was supposed to be the son of a god.

In the play, the role of Minos is hard to act: at the beginning of the play he is sane, but by the end he has descended into madness. The actor playing him needs to decide how his madness develops and how best to show it.

Read and Discuss   1 Look at three speeches by Minos. What makes him seem mad or sane in each one? Look at:
- his first speech (page 11)
- what he says to Daedalus at the bottom of page 35
- how he greets the Athenians (page 80).

2 How much does Minos change between these three speeches? Look particularly at the scene with Daedalus: compare Daedalus' reactions to Minos here with what he says on page 82. Draw up a list of differences in the way Minos appears to Daedalus in the two scenes.

The reconstructed throne room from the Palace at Knossos, Crete. Was this Minos' home? See page 125.

Act

1 Work in pairs: an actor and a director. The actor tries saying the speeches listed above in different ways, and the director makes suggestions on what works best. Remember, Minos is not the same throughout the play – you need to decide how best to show how he changes from speech to speech.

2 Choose three people to act out the scene between Minos and Theseus on pages 86–87 in front of the class. One person plays Theseus; the other two play Minos in different ways. One of them has to overact and shout and make Minos as outwardly mad as possible. The other one has to act as subtly as possible, and play Minos very calmly. Then, as a class, discuss which style of performance is more effective and why. Does one version make you more scared of Minos? Does one make him seem funny?

The Minor Characters

Phaedra and Androgeus

Talk and Write

Phaedra and Androgeus are rather strange individuals, even in a story set many years in the past. What would they be like now?

Imagine that one or both of them came to your school, in your class. Decide how they would be likely to behave. Do you think they would be popular or unpopular? What would you think of them?

1 Write a letter to a magazine's problem page about them. Remember that these letters are quite short: try to write no more than 100 words. Try to express yourself clearly. You need to include:
   - exactly what the problem is
   - what you think about it
   - a request for help to find a solution.
2 Now swap letters with a partner and write the agony aunt's reply to your partner's letter. Remember, the only information the agony aunt has about the situation is what is in the letter.

Act and Discuss

Look at Act 3, Scene 3, where Phaedra and Androgeus threaten the Nurse. Should this scene be funny, or creepy, or both? If both, where does the atmosphere change?

Try acting out the scene in groups of four: three actors and an observer. The actors try out different ways of building up the atmosphere and the observer helps to decide what works best. Some ideas:
   - How should Phaedra and Androgeus move (a) when they are threatening the Nurse, and (b) when they are pleading with her?
   - How does the Nurse react to their behaviour? Does her reaction change during the course of the scene?

If you find it tricky working with the script, improvise *around* the scene from the play. This may give you extra ideas.

. . . .

The Bandits

Read and Discuss   In classical tragedy, there are often comic moments or scenes which
lighten the mood for a while. This gives the audience a change of
atmosphere. Providing a break from the darker parts of the action can
also intensify the more dramatic sections of the play. Some of the
scenes with Phaedra and Androgeus can be seen as working in this
way, and so can the interlude with the bandits in Act 2, Scene 1.

Cast and Block   Look closely at the scene with the bandits:

Periphetes   Cercyon
Sinis   Sciron
The Crommyonian Sow   Procrustes

They all behave in slightly different ways, and are given short
character descriptions. How would you work to make them as
different from each other as possible?

1   Divide the class into six groups. Each group brainstorms a list of
    observations about one of the six characters, both their personality and
    their physical shape. Include reasons.
2   Display all the lists at the front of the class. Do they give you ideas of
    how to make the bandits different from each other? Some lists may not
    give you a clear idea of the physical shape of a character. Think about
    this as a class. Can you come up with a shape that works and that
    makes that character different from the others?
3   Look back at the notes you made about Theseus' character. What
    should he look like? Should he be bigger than all the bandits? If not,
    how should he be different?
4   Cast Theseus and the bandits from the class, picking people who are
    (or can pretend to be) the right physical type for each character.
5   Block the scene with these six and Theseus. ('Blocking' is deciding
    how characters will move on the stage.) Think about
    • how each character moves, based on their shape and personality
    • how to fit the action around the words spoken in the play
    • whether you can add extra 'business' to make the scene as funny
      as possible.

Staging the Play

The Chorus

Classical Greek drama uses a Chorus to link the action together, to provide extra information and strengthen the atmosphere of the play. In using a Chorus in his play of the Greek legend, David Calcutt has created opportunities for an extra view of the action, in a similar way.

Discuss

1 In Greek drama, the Chorus would usually be all male. How do you think the best Chorus would be made up today? Why?
2 In this play, there are two Choruses, one Athenian and the other Cretan. We can often tell where we are by which Chorus is present. How would you make sure the audience could tell the two Choruses apart? You could do this by cast (who makes up each Chorus) or by how the two Choruses are dressed. What would be most effective?

Changing Roles

Design/Staging

At various points in the play, the Chorus 'become people'. Look at the scenes where this happens:

- Act 1, Scene 3: the Cretan Chorus become courtiers; the Athenian Chorus become the jury at Daedalus' trial
- Act 2, Scene 1: the Athenian Chorus become the bandits (unless you use separate actors)
- Act 3, Scenes 2, 4, 7, 9: the Athenian Chorus become the volunteers who go to Crete with Theseus
- Act 3, Scene 2: the Cretan Chorus become the sailors coming from Crete
- Act 3, Scene 4: the Cretan Chorus become the Cretan public wondering at Theseus and the Athenians.

On some of these occasions you may want to change the appearance of the Chorus, in order to show that they are now playing different roles.

Decide *when* you need to make a change – write a list.

Then decide *how* you are going to change the way they look – e.g., by:

- costume changes (but remember, elaborate costume changes will slow the performance down – think of simple changes you could make to costume)

- use of props
- how the Chorus might move and speak when they take on a different role.

A masked chorus, from a modern performance of an ancient Greek play

Masks

Design

In Greek drama, the Chorus often wear masks. This makes them symbolic rather than 'real people'. Would this be appropriate for the Choruses here? If so, how would you make the two sets of masks different?

The Minotaur and the Sow will also need masks. How realistic or stylized should they be? You may need to think quite hard about the mask for Asterius: should it show in some way the complexity of his character?

1   Before you start to design how your mask is going to look, form groups and make a prototype mask, to test the practical aspects. This does not need to be decorated – but it does need to be worn. Try to answer these questions:
    - How big/heavy can a mask be? (Someone has to wear it!)
    - How do you attach it to the wearer? (A mask for an actor who has to fight needs to be very secure.)
    - Where do you put eye-holes?
    - How do you make sure the actor wearing the mask can breathe and make his/her voice heard?
    - How do you make sure the wearer can hear other people in the play?

2 Once you have your prototype shape, choose a mask which you are going to design – it could be for one of the Choruses, for the Sow, for Asterius the Minotaur, or for another character. Start by making a sketch of your mask, based on the prototype your group developed. Label your diagram to show which materials you would use – if you can, attach samples of the materials themselves, and colour swatches.

3 Make the masks and practise using them: do the actors wearing them need to speak more clearly than others without masks? Should they move differently as well as wearing masks?

Scenery

Draw

1 The play of *The Labyrinth* is set in several different locations: Crete, Athens, the Pythoness' cave, Troezen, Sphaeria, the entrance to the labyrinth, Naxos, the Athenian cliffs. Can you pick out key items to make into simple scenery to represent these places? (For example, a few palm fronds could represent Naxos, and a column the temple of Sphaeria.) Remember to keep your ideas simple, as changing scenery can seriously interrupt the action in a play.

2 Can you think of other scenery that could be used to make a dramatic effect in key scenes? Here are some ideas you could try out:
   - sails for the arrival of the Cretan ships at Athens
   - banners for celebrations on Crete, for the arrival of the Athenians who will be sacrificed to the Minotaur
   - banners for Theseus' coronation.

   Think what colour these might be, and how they would be decorated. Draw sketches of these, to show how they might work.

Poster

Design

Look back at all the things you have drawn, created and designed for the play. What is the strongest image to represent the play? Can you find a line of text or a slogan to go with it? Base a poster design around these elements.

Theseus and the Labyrinth: the Original Story

David Calcutt has constructed a new version of the story in order to turn it into a play. There are a few different versions of the original Greek legend, but the basis is always the same.

Crete and Athens

The war between Crete and Athens began when King Minos' son Androgeus came to Athens to compete in some athletic games organized by Aegeus. Androgeus won every event he entered, and Aegeus became jealous of him. So Aegeus sent Androgeus to fight a bull that had been terrorizing the plains of Marathon for some years, and the young man was killed. Minos at once attacked Athens with a fleet of ships. After a long time, Athens was defeated, and Minos ordered the city to pay a tribute to him every year: seven young men and seven young women, who would sail to Crete, never to be seen again. They were food for the Minotaur, the unnatural child of Minos' wife Pasiphae, which was half human, half bull.

The Minotaur lived in a maze-like labyrinth, which had been built by the craftsman Daedalus. Daedalus is supposed to have invented many tools, like the axe and the saw. He fled to Crete from Athens when he was accused of killing his nephew, Talos, a rival inventor. Daedalus designed the labyrinth to be so confusing that even if the Minotaur did not find its victims at once, they could never find their way out.

Read and Discuss

1 Characters are not fleshed out in the legend as they are in the play, but it is quite possible to see that sometimes they are motivated differently from in the play. Think about Minos in the legend and the play. Why does he ask for the tribute from Athens, (a) in the original legend, and (b) in the play? (Look at Act 3, Scene 2 for the answer in the play.)

2 What does this difference make you think of Minos? Write a list of words or phrases that relate to each version of the king. Which version is more sympathetic, and why?

3 Which version of Minos do you think is most effective? Would the play be better if he were more sympathetic?

Theseus goes to Athens

The original story of Theseus' birth and youth is very similar to the play – until his arrival in Athens. When he came to the palace, Aegeus was holding a feast. Although no one knew who Theseus was, he was invited to join in. Aegeus' wife, Medea, was instinctively jealous of Theseus, and tried to poison him. Just in time, Aegeus recognized his sandals and his sword, and stopped Medea. He made her leave, which she did, in a chariot pulled by dragons. Aegeus shared power with Theseus from then on.

A reconstruction of a traditional Greek ship. The ship that took Theseus to Crete might have looked something like this.

Theseus decided to go to Crete and put an end to the tribute of youths and maidens. As he left, he promised his father that if he was successful, he would change the ship's black sail to a white one on his return.

Discuss

Why do you think David Calcutt left out the incident at Athens when Theseus arrived and Medea tried to poison him?

Improvise

Improvise the scene from the original legend showing Theseus' arrival in Athens.

1 In a group, decide what are the key dramatic points in the action: for example, Theseus' entrance, Medea's exit.
2 Decide on what characters to show in the improvisation. There could be quite a lot of people present, or you could focus just on a few characters. Characters you could include: Aegeus, Theseus, Medea, guests at the banquet, palace guards.
3 While you are acting, each think about your character and how they might react to the situation. Would their reactions change at different points in the action?
4 When you have finished, discuss as a class whether you would have included this scene in the play.

Theseus on Crete

When Theseus arrived on Crete, Minos' daughter Ariadne fell in love with him, and decided to help him. She asked Daedalus for advice, and he recommended giving Theseus a ball of thread to help him find his way back out of the labyrinth. Ariadne gave Theseus the thread, and made him promise to take her away with him if he succeeded. He killed the Minotaur, escaped from the labyrinth and took Ariadne with him – but left her behind on the island of Naxos. She was very upset, but was comforted by the god Dionysus, who noticed her on the island, fell in love with her and took her away.

Theseus continued his journey home to Athens, but forgot to change the sail on his ship. Aegeus saw the black sail, and was filled with sorrow, believing he had lost his son. He threw himself into the sea. An oracle's prophecy that he would die of grief had come true.

Read and Write

1 Ariadne here is very different from in the play: she is motivated purely by love for Theseus. Imagine what this Ariadne feels and write three entries for her diary:
   - when she first sees Theseus with the Athenians and falls for him;
   - when she realizes that he will need help and decides to provide it;
   - when she realizes that Theseus has deserted her on Naxos.
   You will need to add extra details, e.g. when and where Ariadne sees Theseus for the first time, as the legend does not give us very much information.
2 Read what you wrote for Ariadne's letter (see page 109). How similar are the two versions of Ariadne? Which one do you like best and why?

Daedalus and Icarus

Meanwhile, Minos was furious at Daedalus for having helped Theseus. He imprisoned Daedalus in the labyrinth he had made, along with his son Icarus. Daedalus knew they had to escape from Crete, and he set to work. First he found a way out of the labyrinth (having designed it, he knew his way around). Then he made two pairs of wings out of feathers held together with wax. When the wings were ready, he and Icarus set out across the sky. Daedalus warned Icarus not to fly too high up, as the sun's heat might melt the wax. But Icarus was so excited by flying that he flew higher and higher, closer and closer to the sun. The wax holding the feathers together melted, and the wings fell apart. Icarus fell into the sea and was drowned. Daedalus reached the land alone.

'The Fall of Icarus', by
the seventeenth-century
artist Carlo Saraceni

Write

Write a short story version of the Daedalus and Icarus tale, focusing on Daedalus' relationship with his son. Write the story from Daedalus' point of view. You could use these sentences as the beginning or end of your story:

> Daedalus took off his wings and looked out over the sea. 'Icarus?' he called, 'where are you?'

Some things you will need to decide:

- How old is Icarus when they come to Crete? At the end of the story?
- Does Icarus' mother feature in the story at all? If so, who was she and why didn't she come to Crete?
- Does Icarus help his father building the labyrinth and making the wings? Or does he get in the way?

Write

1 In two groups, write newspaper reports of Daedalus' life on Crete (why he came there, what he did and how he escaped). One group should write the version with Icarus, the other the version without him. Here are the headlines for the two articles:

> Master Craftsman escapes Crete, loses son

> Labyrinth Designer flees – on wings

2 Swap and read each other's reports. Does Daedalus emerge as a different character in the two different versions?

Talk

Icarus has been left out of the play, although he is a very popular character in tellings of the story. Why do you think the author has left Icarus out? Does it have an effect on the way we see Daedalus?

Theseus the King

Theseus reigned as king of Athens for many years and had a son called Hippolytus. Hippolytus dedicated himself to Artemis, the goddess of hunting, and swore never to marry.

Theseus later married Phaedra, Ariadne's sister, and she fell for Hippolytus. She approached him, but he rejected her. Full of spite, she told Theseus that Hippolytus had tried to rape her. He cursed his son, and asked the god Poseidon to punish him. Hippolytus was killed by a sea monster as he drove his chariot along the shore. Phaedra admitted the truth, and killed herself, leaving Theseus full of grief at what he had been led to do.

Discuss and Write

1 Think about Theseus' public image as a king, based on the legend. What aspects of his life would he be proud of and publicize? What things would he keep secret? Make two lists, and for each item, say why Theseus would want people to know (or not know) about it.

2 Divide the class in two. Each half will write the script for a TV news report on Theseus' death, summing up his character and life achievements. One half will write for an Athenian TV station, and the other for a Cretan channel. Think before you start:
   - Will your viewers be sympathetic towards Theseus or not?
   - What things will people know and not know? (Look at your list, and remember some things might only be known as rumours.)
   - Pick out high points and low points of Theseus' story.
   - Interview other people – e.g. Minos, Ariadne, Daedalus – for their reactions to Theseus' death.

If you have a camcorder, try recording your news report.

What the Author Says

Why did you choose this story to make into a play?

There are certain stories I carry around in my head that for one reason or another I'm attracted to – or they attract themselves to me. This particular story – the story of Theseus and the Minotaur, Daedalus and the labyrinth – has had been with me for a long time. I think it was one of the first Greek myths I came across as a child, and it's held a particular fascination since then.

What attracted you in particular to the legend?

For a start, it's a terrific story – full of thrilling incidents and memorable characters. Easily as exciting as *Star Wars*. But I think it's more than that. And what makes it more than just an adventure story is the creature around which the whole story revolves, the Minotaur, squatting there at the centre in the dark with its man's body and bull's head. I've always found that image particularly fascinating. The idea of a creature that's both human and animal at the same time.

You left out Theseus' arrival at Athens and Medea's attempt on his life – why?

I left out the Medea section simply for reasons of length, which was a shame, because it would have made for good drama. Medea is a powerful character, but the whole story of her attempting to poison Theseus, then being found out, and then escaping in a chariot pulled by dragons, would have added too much to the length of the play. And it would have delayed Theseus' leaving for Crete, which I needed to get to as quickly as possible.

What about Icarus? What made you decide not to include him?

Including Icarus would have meant either lengthening the play, or leaving out something else that I felt was more important. And I wanted Daedalus to be an isolated character, an outlaw, an outsider. Giving him a son, whom he loves, would have taken some of that from him. Also he's the only one in the play who gets away without losing anything. If I'd included Icarus, and Icarus' death, he would have lost something, and I wanted to portray Daedalus as the eternal winner. The little winged figure Daedalus makes for Ariadne is all that's left of Icarus.

What other changes did you make to the original story?

The characters in myth are nothing more than ciphers, archetypes – Hero, Monster, Princess, King, and so on. They represent aspects of human nature, but they're not actually real human beings in themselves. That's the way myths work. But in a play, if we're to identify with the characters on-stage, they have to be believable as human beings.

So, I don't think I changed the characters so much as tried to make them into people we can believe in and, as I said, people we can identify with when we see them on-stage. Otherwise we won't engage emotionally with the story, and that's something that has to happen in a play.

So which characters did you alter?

The first character I concentrated on was the Minotaur. In the myth, and in every version of the story that I've read, he's simply a beast, a monster who only exists so that Theseus can kill him. My decision to make him more than that arose from something very practical and simple. I wanted to give the actor playing the Minotaur something more to do than just stand there in a mask and roar. I wanted to give him something to say, a voice in the play. And giving him a voice meant giving him a personality. What kind of personality, though? While I was thinking about this, it struck me that the obvious thing about the Minotaur was that it was part-beast and part-man, a creature with a beast's head and a man's body. In other words, a creature with the mind and instincts of an animal, but the heart and spirit of a human being; a creature that's aware of, and in conflict with itself. And this made it a creature for whom we could feel sympathy. But in order to show this, I needed a character with whom the Minotaur could interact onstage, a character who would also feel sympathy with him. I chose Ariadne for this purpose, and this gave me a clue as to how I should develop her character.

But if she felt sympathy for the Minotaur, how would she then feel about Theseus, and why should she help him kill her brother? In the myth, it's because she falls in love with him, but this wasn't in keeping with the character of Ariadne in the play. Besides, making the Minotaur sympathetic made Theseus into something more than a monster-slaying hero. He became a rather cold-hearted killer, a man completely fixed on his own purpose, with no real feeling for anyone else. Something of an anti-hero, in fact. So I had to come up with another reason for Ariadne to help this heartless warrior kill her brother, and go away with him. And this had to be that the situation she lived in had become so unbearable that she'd do anything to escape it. And that suggested the idea of making her brother and sister cruel and disturbed, and her father a deranged tyrant.

So, the characterisation for most of the major characters grew out of that single decision to give the Minotaur a voice. And that was how I proceeded with the other characters – letting a single decision make other decisions for me, so that the characters developed as I was writing them.

Who is your favourite character, and why?

My favourite character in the play is Daedalus. I've always found him appealing, because, unlike many other characters in myth, he's not a hero, or a god. He's a craftsman, an inventor, an artist, and that's what he owes his allegiance to – his art. But this gives his nature something of a double edge. Being so dedicated to his art, he's also completely self-centred and self-seeking. And he's an outlaw, too, someone on the run. And an outsider. I've always found those kinds of characters attractive.

He's also one of the few characters in Greek mythology whose end is unknown. The last we hear of him is in Sicily, after he's escaped from the labyrinth, making toys for the king's daughters. When Minos arrives there in pursuit of Daedalus, the king's daughters hide Daedalus, then kill Minos by pouring boiling water into his bath. After that, we hear no more about Daedalus. What happens to him? Does he stay on in Sicily? Or does he go off somewhere else? We don't know. It's as if he just flies out of the story. I seem to remember reading somewhere that there's a tradition of him coming to Britain, and that accounts for the many labyrinth patterns found scratched into the stones of ancient burial chambers. I like that idea.

Arthur Evans and Knossos

Apart from legends, the ancient people of Crete were unknown in the rest of the world from when their civilization collapsed, around 1400 BC, until the early 1900s. That changed because of the work of one man: Arthur Evans.

Arthur Evans was born in 1851. From childhood, he was interested in archaeology: when he was seven, he buried a favourite toy in the garden. In imitation of an Egyptian burial, he put in with the toy various other items and labelled the spot: 'KING EDWARD SIXTH and the butterfly and their cloths and things'. His father mentioned it in his diary, saying that he found Arthur rather hard to understand.

At the age of 32, Arthur Evans went to meet Heinrich Schliemann in Athens. Schliemann was a famous archaeologist who had recently excavated the ancient cities of Troy and Mycenae. While looking around the site of Mycenae, Evans noticed that the style of the architecture was quite different from classical Greek buildings. And he found octopuses in many designs, which he thought was odd for somewhere on the mainland. He wondered where the Mycenean culture could have come from: the islands of Greece?

Nearly ten years later, Evans met another archaeologist, who was very interested in Crete. He had found many Roman and ancient Greek remains on the island, and was sure there were much older things there too. In the meantime, Evans found many strange things in Athenian shops which reminded him of what he had seen at Mycenae. When he asked the shopkeepers about them, they said these things were from Crete.

The ancient Greek writer Homer had referred to Crete's ruler Minos, and said that he lived at Knossos. When Evans had a chance to buy some land on Crete, a quarter of a plot known locally as Knossos, he jumped at the chance. He planned to start digging there as soon as he could. But a war between the Greeks and the Turks kept him away for six years.

At last, on 23 March 1900, digging started. On the second day, the excavators started to find the remains of a house and bits of frescoes (paintings made on plaster walls, when the plaster was still wet). Evans soon knew he had found what he was looking for.

In early April, the spades dug into a chamber with benches and a carved stone throne. The room had clearly contained wooden columns, which had burnt in a great fire. More and more rooms were uncovered, with passageways and staircases between them; in the first season of digging, over two acres of palace were found.

Evans took on a skilled painter to replace or restore frescoes, and reconstructed the rooms the team had excavated. Many of the frescoes showed bulls, which were also seen charging across the sides of vases. One of the most famous images from Knossos is the bull-leaping fresco, which shows three young people apparently vaulting over a powerful bull. It is not known whether this represents a sport, an entertainment or a fictional scene. But it is clearly a powerful image and a very important one to the Minoans, as Evans decided to call them, after their legendary king Minos.

The famous 'bull-leaping fresco' from Knossos

Write

1 Look at the bull-leaping fresco. Was it a sport – more dangerous than bull-fighting – or was it an imagined scene? Write down your impressions of the young Minoans and the sport they are involved in.
2 Imagine you are one of Arthur Evans' excavators, finding this picture in the ground. You would be the first person to see it for 3000 years. Describe finding the picture and how you see it.

Going Underground

In 1901, Evans bought the rest of the site. In this season of digging, the men found a huge staircase, with steps going up and down. Eventually the Grand Staircase, as it came to be called, was completely uncovered: four complete flights of stairs and a hint that

A reconstruction
of the Palace at
Knossos

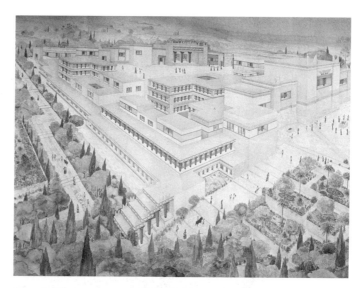

there had once been a fifth flight on top. The palace was not only huge in area, it had also had many storeys. And throughout the timbers had been destroyed by fire, so clearly the palace had come to a dramatic end.

From what he found at Knossos, Evans concluded that the civilization on Crete was at its peak in about 1600BC, and that the palace was destroyed in about 1400BC. The area around Crete suffers from earthquakes, so it was probably an earthquake that destroyed the city, followed by fire. But who really knows?

Write

Imagine you are one of the people working on Arthur Evans' dig at Knossos. You have uncovered a room with a beautiful patterned floor. The pattern seems to weave in and out, showing a sort of maze. As you sweep the dust away from this floor, you notice a shape in the middle – it is a trapdoor. You open it and see steps leading down.

Write a story of what happens, starting from when you decide to go down the steps. Try to build up a strong atmosphere. Remember:
- use all your senses: what can you see, hear, feel, smell?
- don't tell the reader too much: leave some things to their imagination to make it really creepy
- is it scarier to see a monster or to simply sense that it is there?

Plays in this series include:

Across the Barricades   ISBN 0 19 831272 5
  Joan Lingard   adapted by David Ian Neville

The Bonny Pit Laddie   ISBN 0 19 831278 4
  Frederick Grice   adapted by David Spraggon Williams with Frank Green

The Burston School Strike   ISBN 0 19 831274 1
  Roy Nevitt

The Canterbury Tales   ISBN 0 19 831293 8
  Geoffrey Chaucer   adapted by Martin Riley

Carrie's War   ISBN 0 19 831295 4
  Nina Bawden   adapted by Robert Staunton

The Demon Headmaster   ISBN 0 19 831270 9
  Gillian Cross   adapted by Adrian Flynn

Dracula   ISBN 0 19 831456 6
  Bram Stoker   adapted by David Calcutt

Frankenstein   ISBN 0 19 831267 9
  Mary Shelley   adapted by Philip Pullman

Hot Cakes   ISBN 0 19 831273 3
  Adrian Flynn

Jane Eyre   ISBN 0 19 831296 2
  Charlotte Brontë   adapted by Steve Barlow and Steve Skidmore

Johnny and the Dead   ISBN 0 19 831294 6
  Terry Pratchett   adapted by Stephen Briggs

The Labyrinth   ISBN 0 19 831458 2
  David Calcutt

Paper Tigers   ISBN 0 19 831268 7
  Steve Barlow and Steve Skidmore

A Question of Courage   ISBN 0 19 831271 7
  Marjorie Dark   adapted by Bill Lucas and Brian Keaney

Smith   ISBN 0 19 831297 0
  Leon Garfield   adapted by Robert Staunton

A Tale of Two Cities   ISBN 0 19 831292 X
  Charles Dickens   adapted by Steve Barlow and Steve Skidmore

Tess of the D'Urbervilles   ISBN 0 19 831439 6
  Thomas Hardy   adapted by David Calcutt

The Turbulent Term of Tyke Tiler   ISBN 0 19 831269 5
  adapted from her own novel by Gene Kemp